To: BOB MA____E
A G___ FRIEND,
A TRUE P____EER Too
AUTOMATION in CzecHoSLovAKIA

_erry Murphy SHEFFIELD

BRATISLAVIA
SEPT. 12, 1989

66 centuries of measurement

This book was commissioned by the Sheffield Corporation in 1955 and was first published in serial form in THE SHEFFIELDER, a quarterly publication, under the original title, "History of Metrology." It was then presented in pocket form in 1960, entitled 66 CENTURIES OF MEASUREMENT. In 1984, the book has been completely updated by a team of dedicated Sheffield engineers. It is presented here in the hope of inviting readership among non-technical people as well as engineers.

preface to the third edition

Although the word "metrology" has for a long time been one of the 600,000 words which make up the English language, it is only in the past few decades that it emerged into general usage.

It is derived from two Greek words: metron, a measure of length; and logos. Logos originally meant "word," but its meaning gradually shifted to "reason" — hence, "logic." According to Webster, metrology is the science of, or system of weights and measures. In fact, the word metrology is often confused with meteorology, but in few instances can two additional vowels make such a wide difference in meaning.

The average man takes measurement for granted. To him, it connotes a foot rule, a pocket tape, or perhaps a micrometer, but hardly anything worthy of profound consideration. When he becomes a manufacturer or scientist, or engineer or navigator, or philosopher, he comes to realize that measurement is basic to an exact knowledge of his environment and to his ability to cope with that environment. Measurement is one of the principal tools of discovery, and it is essential for mass production. Man's physical standard of living has always advanced in direct proportion to his ability to reduce progressively the quotient of the inch.

Behind today's rapidly shrinking dimensional tolerances stretch six milleniums of human endeavor in the study and application of measurement — its romances, its tragedies, it accomplishments.

In the spring of 1955 Louis Polk, President of the Sheffield Corporation, authorized the preparation of a History of Metrology to supplement previous literature in this field. The second edition was commissioned in 1984 by John Bosch, Vice-president and General Manager when the name Sheffield was returned to the business after being purchased by the Cross & Trecker Corporation from Allied/Bendix.

In carrying out this project the objective has been to tell the story of dimensional measurement as far as possible from the human interest angle, and without undue emphasis on technicalities.

FIRST PRINTING, October 1984

Price: $14.50 — Additional copies may be obtained by writing The Sheffield Measurement Division — Advertising Department, P.O. Box 1127, Dayton, Ohio 45401

foreword

While this book covers 66 Centuries of dimensional measurement, the preparation of the second edition has brought into focus the rapid advancement in metrology during the 25 years since the first edition was published. Of particular significance is the fact that during this relatively short time interval there have been two changes in the standard for length used by the National Bureau of Standards and similar institutions throughout the world. A few years after the first edition was published they changed to a wave length of light as a basic standard measurement of length. More recently, in 1983, they converted to the use of an atomic clock in conjunction with light traveling in a vacuum. The atomic clock has an accuracy of one second in 300,000 years. Using time as a basis for measuring length demonstrates the progress made by scientists in refining accuracy in metrology. Similar progress has been made in the development of advanced dimensional measurement equipment for our more automated factories.

This book is a tribute to the engineers and scientists at Sheffield whose skills, leadership, talents and dedication to metrology have contributed so much to this progress.

Future advancements in dimensional measurement will help accelerate improvements in productivity and thus the quality of life throughout the world.

October 1984

John A. Bosch
Dayton, Ohio

The cubit, dating back at least to the Khufu Pyramid, was the first known standard of measurement. It was used with remarkable accuracy in building all the great pyramids.

the beginning

We can only speculate on how man came to conceive the idea of measurement. The underlying reasons doubtless were his inherent curiosity and the constant urge to improve his mode of living. Also, his determination to improvise whatever means were needed to achieve each step in his continued progress. Very early in his development man began to wonder "why."

The only tangible basis for speculating on the events which led to the concept of measurement is the meager evidence turned up from time to time by archaeologists, chiefly in Mesopotamia and Eqypt.

Probably the first significant event in human progress was the transition from food gathering to food producing. In short, the birth of agriculture.

Agriculture, Architecture and Real Property

The Stone Age cave dweller doubtless came to the conclusion that he could achieve a more abundant life if he supplemented the food supplied by forest and stream by what he himself could grow. In order to do this, he found it expedient to abandon his cave home and seek more fertile land for his simple crops. This he seems to have found on the alluvial plains of the Tigris and Euphrates — probably about 6000 B.C.

Having forsaken his ancestral caves, man found it necessary to improvise some other type of shelter. Thus, the beginnings of architecture and the trend toward village life. This is reflected in the archaeological discoveries at Jarmo, Hassuna and Halaf in the Tigris Valley. Similar progress seems to have been made in the valley of the upper Nile.

The demands of this budding agricultural economy could hardly be satisfied by the crude eoliths, or crude stone tools, of former days. A greater number and variety of tasks demanded more efficient tools.

To the simple mud hearth dwelling a roof was added. Dried mud gave way to timber, brick and stone. Handfitting and therefore sighting or eye measurement became necessary. Land ownership required some kind of understandable property description. In a word, civilization had begun.

It is incredible that such a train of events could fail to suggest a need for a definite means of size comparison, at least for the purposes of construction and the description of real property. The need for units of measurement was probably realized before 5000 B.C.

The Cubit — First Unit of Measure

Following his natural instinct and ego, man selected his own body as a basis for the first units of measure — the length of his forearm, foot, hand, and finger. Such units were always available and were easily understood. Of these, the cubit (the distance from the elbow to the end of the outstretched middle finger) became the most widely used throughout the ancient world. The Egyptians attributed authorship of their weights and measures to their god Thoth while the Greeks attributed theirs to Mercury.

M. Bertillon has since proved that the length of the human forearm or cubit is fairly constant. While it varies with individuals, once a man has reached maturity, there is no further change.

The earliest authentic unit of length is the Royal Egyptian Cubit, known to have been in use at the time the Khufu Pyramid was constructed (2750 B.C.), and mentioned in connection with the building of Noah's Ark.

Careful measurement of the Khufu Pyramid at Gizeh which measures about 756 feet on each side and is 481 feet high, shows a mean error in the length of the sides of only 0.6 inch and an error in angle from a perfect square of only 12 seconds.

There is also good reason to believe a cubit was the unit used in Babylonia and by the ancient Jews.

The cubit was inherited by the Greeks and the Romans, but, from archaeological evidence, none of these cubits agreed in actual length. The Royal Egyptian Cubit seems to have been approximately equal to 20.62 of our inches. The Greek cubit was 2.38 inches shorter. The area of a square on the Greek Olympic Cubit is equal to that of a circle having a diameter of one Royal Egyptian Cubit. If this is a coincidence, it is a very interesting one.

As far as is known, the Greeks were the first to subdivide the cubit. They broke it down into two spans, six palms or twenty-four digits. The Romans in turn took the Greek Olympic Cubit, but subdivided it according to their own ideas into twelve thumb nail breadths or unciae.

First Legal Code

There is what remains of a sun-baked clay tablet in the museum at Istanbul which was written by a scribe in cuneiform about 2050 B.C. It is the oldest written law code known to man, antedating that of Hammurabi by some 300 years. These laws promulgated by the Sumerian King Ur-Nammu contain a reference to honest weights and measures.

Britain's Stonehenge

Stonehenge, on the Salisbury Plain, Wiltshire, one of the mysteries of British antiquity, is interesting for a number of reasons. One is that its huge stones were placed by careful measurement. Archaeologists have fairly well established by means of radioactive examination that the original construction was done in the late Neolithic period, perhaps 2000 B.C. Further, the unit of measure used in laying out the arrangement of the stones was the Phoenician Foot. Additions were made later in the Bronze Age, apparently using the Pelasgo-Roman Foot.

Egyptian Mathematics

The Rhind Papyrus, written in Egypt about 1700 B.C. has now been deciphered and proves to be a mathematical handbook of considerable merit even by our standards.

Early Commerce and Manufacture

The beginnings of commerce and manufacture are lost in antiquity; from archaeological evidence, however, commerce probably originated in the Tigris-Euphrates Valleys and in Egypt where the first merchants relied on protected caravans to transport their merchandise, including manufactured goods.

Later the Cretan, Egyptian, and Phoenician merchants took to the sea in expanding their trade routes, sometime before 1600 B.C.

Inscriptions on the tomb of Queen Hatsheput of Egypt describe a voyage (1500 B.C.) of her merchantmen from Thebes on the upper Nile to the Somali Coast of the Red Sea for a cargo of incense.

In all probability, manufacturing developed concurrently with commerce. Not only manufacturing, but the concept of division of labor.

The Division of Labor

A painting on the wall of the tomb of Reklmara, prefect of Thebes about 1600 B.C., illustrates manufacturing in which each process is carried on by its own workman or group of workmen.

In the 5th century B.C., Xenophon wrote: "It is impossible for a man to work at many things and do them all well; but in the great cities, because there are numbers that want each particular thing, one art alone suffices for the maintenance of each individual. One man gets maintenance merely by stitching shoes, another by cutting them out, another by simply putting together the pieces. He, therefore, that is employed in a work of the smallest compass must, of a necessity, do it best."

The Iron Age and Tools

As long as man's only tools were of stone, bone, or wood, their exact size was of little importance. When he started using metal he soon discovered that he could control size and could duplicate any tool that had proved exceptionally effective. Thus began what has come to be the happy marriage of tools and metrology, whose progeny has lead civilization's advancement ever since. For the past two centuries tools and precision have been so closely integrated that it would be unrealistic to treat them separately.

Copper and bronze originated this phase of development, but the advent of iron brought vast new possibilities and greatly increased the scope of tools and instruments.

Rome and the Iron Age entered history at about the same time —

4

1000 B.C., although it is not to be inferred that iron was unknown and unused prior to that. In fact Egyptians had made small ornaments of hematite more than two milleniums before. Within the last thirty years an iron dagger has been unearthed in the ruins of the ancient holy city of Eshnunna (2700 B.C.), but not until 1000 B.C. was iron widely used in the Mediterranean world.

Archimedes

In Syracuse, until he was murdered by a drunken Roman soldier in 212 B.C., lived Archimedes, the great philosophical mathematician and father of applied mechanics. It was he who discovered the principles and application of hydrostatics, the lever, the pulley, and the screw helix, none of which he considered very important. Geometry was his great love. In fact his inventions and contributions in the field of mechanics were made reluctantly and at the insistence of Hiero, then King of Syracuse.

Archimedes stumbled on the idea of specific gravity almost accidentally. It seems that King Hiero had turned over to his court jeweler a quantity of gold to be used in making a royal crown. On its completion, Hiero, suspicious of the jeweler's integrity, commissioned Archimedes to determine whether the new crown contained all the gold originally provided, or whether the craftsman had substituted silver to appropriate some of the more valuable metal for himself.

Without a knowledge of analytical chemistry, Archimedes faced a tough assignment. His great inspiration came as he noticed the water in his bath tub overflow as he climbed in on one of those rare occasions when he was prevailed upon to take a bath. He instantly recognized the principle of specific gravity and its ideal application to the difficult problem at hand. Without waiting for either the bath or his clothes, he was so anxious to test his theory, he raced back home naked crying "Eureka, Eureka!" (I have found it!)

Archimedes used the helix principle, hitherto unrecognized, to remove bilge water from Hiero's ships. His device consisted of a tube wound on a helix around a cylinder. With the lower end of the cylinder submerged, rotating it about its axis raised the water in the tube and discharged it at the upper end.

Roman Contributions

Roman artificers almost immediately recognized the possibilities of the screw principle and its application to their work. Thus the screw thread began to replace the wedge as a fastener.

The first screws were made of wood by filing or carving the threads free hand. Metal screws were originally made in the same way or by soldering a wire, wrapped helix fashion, around a rod. Examples of these old Roman screws have been found in the ruins of Pompeii and in other parts of the world.

With the rise of Rome, its zest for conquest and colonization focused attention on longer units of measure. Thus, the "mille," 1000 paces or double steps, became the Roman statute mile. Again the unit of measure was predicated on the human body.

The commerce of Rome and Phoenicia flourished concurrently and their manufacturing progressed. Angular measurement was well understood. The length of the solar year had been computed to within 7 hours of its true value. Before the Christian Era began, the circumference of the earth had been measured with an error of only about 50 miles.

When Rome was sacked by the Goths under Alaric in 410 A.D., and shortly thereafter by the Vandals under Genseric, Europe began its decline into the Dark Ages.

Gradually the standards and the craftsmanship of Rome were forgotten, and likewise progress in metrology. The principal businesses of the new barbarian leaders were war and conquest. Unlike those of the present century, these wars inspired no technical advances which could prove useful in peaceful pursuits.

About all the learning and culture that remained in Europe was confined to the ecclesiastical groups in the monasteries.

The foot was defined as "the length of the actual foot of the ruling monarch."

medieval europe

Except for progress made by the Arabs, and a temporary revival under Charlemagne about 800 A.D., academic progress was practially non-existent.

Arabic Numerals

We are prone to take our system of numerals pretty much for granted, but consider for a moment what a task it would be to dimension a drawing if we were restricted to the cumbersome Roman numerals of about 1100 A.D. As an instance, 2814 would have been expressed as MMDCCCXIIII in Rome at that time.

Our present system came through Arab culture, although it probably originated with the Hindus at still an earlier date.

The earliest European manuscript bearing Arabic numerals was written in Spain about 976 A.D. It was more than 600 years later that the decimal point, as we know it, came into use.

Saxon England

After the Romans evacuated England, political authority there was divided among a number of small-local Saxon kings, who were primarily interested in wars of conquest. The climate for cultural progress did not exist, nor was there any particular need for metrology at that time.

The "Law of Edward," which we shall refer to again later, was an accumulation of Anglo-Saxon law dating from 600 A.D., when the first code was published by Aethelbert, King of Kent. Additions were made by Ine in 690, by Alfred in 900, by Edgar between 959 and 975 and by Canute in 1035.

King Edgar decreed "Let one measure and one weight pass; such as is observed at London and at Winchester."

Norman England

It has been stated by some writers that Henry I (1068-1135), the third of the Norman Kings, standardized the English yard ("Gerde" or "Yerde") as the distance from the tip of his nose to the end of his outstretched thumb. This is questionable. Henry I issued few ordinances and the unofficial compilation known as "Leges Henrici" indicates that his public policy, like that of William the Conqueror, was to maintain the "Law of Edward" or the basic Anglo-Saxon law which already carried reference to standards of measurement.

Under the Normans all legal standards of measurement were transferred to Westminster and placed in the care of the chamberlains of the exchequer. Their dimensions, however, were not changed.

In the Westgate Museum at Winchester there is, according to Berriman, a hexagonal brass rod cataloged as a standard yard of the time of Henry I but having re-standardized ends stamped E (for Edward I) and H (for Henry VII) respectively.

If the brass bar in the Westgate Museum was the one refered to by King Edgar in the 10th century (and there is such a possibility), then this was the first prototype standard of the western world.

With war the principal order of business at that time, and in view of the difficulties that beset the traveler, the importance of a prototype standard is questionable regardless of its location.

The "Iron Ulna" and the Three Barleycorns

Published accounts have appeared from time to time of the "Iron Ulna" of Edward I and the "Three Barleycorns" of his successor Edward II.

There was a legal standard known as the Iron Ulna and also a statute defining the inch as the length of three barleycorns. But considerable doubt exists as to who was as responsible for these standards.

Several compilations of English law dating back to the code of Aethelbert King of Kent (560-616) have been published. The one which is accepted as authoritative by the British Government was made by the Commissioners of Public Records (1810-1828).

This compilation lists a number of ordinances as being of uncertain date but enacted the century starting with the coronation of Henry III and ending with the death of Edward II. That would be from 1227 to 1327. The following are pertinent sections from these ordinances:

(a) Statutum de Admensuratione Terre (Statute for Measuring of Land):

"And it is to be remembered that the Iron Ulna of our Lord the King contains three feet and no more; and the foot must contain twelve inches, measured by the correct measure of this kind of ulna; that is to say, one thirty-sixth part the said ulna makes one inch, neither more nor less. And 5-1/2 ulna, or 16-1/2 feet, make one perch in accordance with the above-described Iron Ulna of our Lord the King."

(b) Compositio Ulnarum et Perticarum (Composition — or Size — of Ulna and Perch):

"It is ordained that three grains of barley, dry and round, make an inch; twelve inches make a foot; three feet make an ulna; 5-1/2 ulna make a perch; and forty perches in length and four perches in breadth make an acre."

The Record Commissioners indicate that in some early editions of the British statutes these two ordinances were combined into one; however, their own authoritative compilation lists them as two separate statutes, both of uncertain date, and belonging to the time of Henry III, Edward I, or Edward II. Most of the earlier sources also list the dates of these statutes as uncertain, although one comprehensive listing of British laws assigns the Statute of Measuring of Land to the 33rd year of Edward I (1305).

The second statute is listed as being of uncertain date by Ruffhead as well as by the Record Commissioners. Neither source, nor any other compilation, lists the date 1324 for the "three barleycorns equal one inch" statute, although this date is quite commonly cited by historians.

From a study of the personal characteristics and accomplishments of these three monarchs it is difficult to conceive how either Henry III or Edward II could have been much concerned with standards of measurement. On the other hand, Edward I was definitely interested in the land laws of England. It seems, therefore, quite possible that Edward I, far more capable than either his predecessor or his successor, was responsible for both ordinances in question.

On that supposition, it seems natural to ask why he courted confusion by defining the inch in more than one way. There is a possibility that the three barleycorns standard was legalized only to aid all those who were unable to make use of a prototype housed at Westminster. After all, in those days high precision was relatively unimportant.

The Yard of Henry VII

There is a reference above to the hexagonal brass standard of the time of Henry I (1068-1135). On the same authority, this prototype was restandardized and its ends stamped with "E" for Edward I and "H" for Henry VII, who reigned from 1485 to 1509. If so, why did Henry VII go back at least 350 years for a standard which, as previously pointed out, may have originated much earlier with King Edgar, when he might just as well have used the more recent "Iron Ulna?" From the early records, we do know that Parliament under Henry VII was much concerned with standards of commerce and manufacture which might conceivably have included weights and measures.

To further complicate the question, we have the seventh report of the "Warden of the Standards" (Great Britain) for 1872. This illustrates an octagonal bar graduated in yards on one side and inches on the other and claimed to be the standard yard of Henry VII.

Strangely enough one end of this bar is stamped with what appears to be an "E" and the other with what might be an "H." Was this a direct copy of the old standard of Edgar and Henry or Edward I? The principal difference seems to be that of the hexagonal versus the octagonal cross section.

Presumably the "Iron Ulna" and the three barleycorns remained the legal standards of Britain at least for the 158 years before Henry VII.

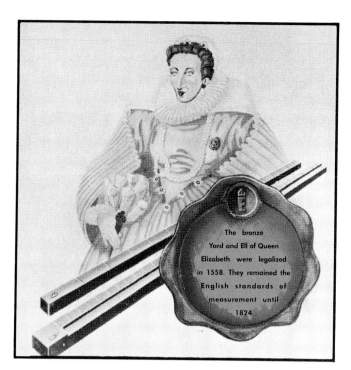

The bronze Yard and Ell of Queen Elizabeth were legalized in 1558. They remained the English standards of measurement until 1824

the renaissance

During this time the Renaissance had begun. Great universities such as Vienna, Heidelberg, Leipzig, and Louvain had been founded. Gutenberg had set up his first printing press.

Leonardo Da Vinci, the great artist, architect, engineer and philosopher was making his immortal reputation. In his notebooks appear several designs for screw cutting machines. The screw, after a thousand years of oblivion, had reappeared in Europe.

By 1360 the first mechanical clock had been built by Henry Wieck of Wurtenberg for Charles V of France.

Gun powder was used for the first time in Europe at the Battle of Crecy in 1346. Thus, ordnance came on the scene.

One of the earliest lathes was presented in 1500 to the Holy Roman Emperor Maximilian I, referred to as the last of the knights and the first of the artillerymen. This lathe, made entirely of wood except for the centers, was operated by a cord wound around the work piece, with one end attached to a foot treadle and the other to a spring pole-overhead. When the treadle reached the floor, the operator backed his tool out and let the spring pole lift the treadle back to its original position, reversing the rotation of the work on its return. By repeating the process, the work piece could finally be finished.

From the death of Henry VII until the accession of Elizabeth to the British throne, a period of 49 years, little of interest in the fields of science and metrology may be noted, except for the monumental work of Copernicus. Sixty odd years before the telescope was invented. Copernicus challenged the accepted Ptolemaic Theory of astronomy and announced the Copernican Theory which has had universal acceptance ever since.

English Rod

An old sixteenth century woodcut shows the English rod being defined by the total length of the left feet of the first sixteen men to come from church on Sunday morning.

The Yard and Ell of Queen Elizabeth

In her busy and intrigue-ridden reign Queen Elizabeth found time to issue new exchequer standards known as the "Yard" and "Ell." The latter was primarily a standard for cloth measurement. Both were end standards, and both are engraved with the initial "E" together with the royal crown.

These remained the legal British standard until 1824 when they were superseded by an Act of Parliament under George IV.

The great accomplishments of this era included those of Galileo Galilei, John Napier, William Gascoigne and Pierre Vernier — accomplishments essential to future progress in metrology.

Galileo

In 1581, when he was seventeen years old, Galileo was not yet acclaimed a great scientist-philosopher. At prayer in the cathedral of Pisa, he became conscious of the annoying rattle of a chain which he saw to be the support of a hanging lamp. It had carelessly been left swinging. Then he noticed that the clicks made by the chain seemed to be rhythmical and regular, even though the arc through which the lamp swung gradually decreased. That was the inspiration which led to his discovery of the primary law of the pendulum, to be used later as the basis for the work of

Huyghens, Picard, and Richter.

Although a Dutch spectacle maker, probably Hans Lippershey, discovered the optical principle of the telescope, it was Galileo who produced the first 32-power telescope in about 1610.

Galileo carried on where Archimedes left off, materially advancing mechanics to the status of a science. He clearly grasped the idea of force as a mechanical agent. He developed the laws of falling bodies and the curve of a projectile in flight.

Napier's Logarithms

John Napier, a Scottish mathematician, in 1614 published his "Canonis Descriptio" embodying his discovery of logarithms. It was Napier, also, who first used the decimal point to express fractions.

The Slide Rule

Using Napier's logarithms, William Oughtred in 1621 devised the first slide rule. The slide rule was used almost universally by engineers until the early 1970's when the electronic calculator became popular.

Gascoigne and the Micrometer

It was William Gascoigne, an astronomer, killed at the age of 24 in one of the battles of the Civil War of 1642, who first used the screw thread as a means of measurement.

Gascoigne had set himself the task of measuring the diameter of the sun, moon, and other celestial bodies by means of a sort of triangulation. This required a very accurate measurement of the diameter of his target at the eyepiece of his telescope, which might have been one that Galileo had built. Any error in the measurement of the image in his telescope he knew would throw his calculations out tremendously.

To a rifleman, a thirty-six inch bullseye at a thousand yards appears about the size of a pea. As the distance increases, the pea gets relatively smaller. Gascoigne figuratively had to measure the pea in order to compute its subtended angle.

The next question was how to measure the image in his telescope. A scale graduated even to hundredths of an inch would have been far too crude. But even if a finer scale had been available, the difficulty in reading it with human eyes would have ruled it out. Another means of measurement was imperative.

Gascoigne solved his problem by devising calipers, the indicating fingers of which were moved simultaneously in opposite directions by a screw having a left hand thread on one end and a right hand thread on the other.

He could measure the number of threads per inch with a graduated scale and thus compute the pitch of the screw. Likewise he could compute the advance for any fractional turn of the screw. Such was the basic idea in 1638 upon which the modern micrometer was based. According to his own records, Gascoigne was able to measure angles to seconds.

It would be natural to ask where Gascoigne got the threaded element for his screw calipers. The record doesn't cover this point, but it is possible that the screw in question was cut on a lathe similar to the one the French engineer Besson built in 1569 — the first machine devised for cutting threads. Besson was able to cut threads of any pitch within reason by means of interchangeable pulleys and a lead screw.

The Vernier Scale

It is doubtful that Gascoigne's screw caliper had a vernier for greater precision in reading. It might have had, for Pierre Vernier in 1631, seven years earlier, had published in Brussels a treatise entitled "Construction Usage et Propietes du Quadrant Noveau de Mathematiques" in which he described the vernier.

Metrology, like other sciences, depends on and is influenced by work and discoveries in other fields more or less closely related. Such is the case with the accomplishments of Huyghens, Picard, and Richter, all of whom made use of Galileo's preliminary work on the basic law of the pendulum.

The Pendulum as a Standard of Measurement

Christiaan Huyghens, a Dutch mathematician, astronomer and physicist, in desperate need of an accurate time piece for astronomical work, either hit upon the pendulum idea himself or borrowed it from a contemporary. Huyghens determined that the pendulum, depending on its length, could be made to beat any desired time interval. In other words the vibration interval of a pendulum is a constant determined by its length. Huyghens built a pendulum-controlled clock and presented it to the States-General in 1657.

Huyghens is also credited with developing the basic wave theory of light in 1665.

Even at this time the concept of a standard of measurement which could be derived from or tied into some natural constant was being considered.

Jean Picard

Jean Picard, probably on the basis of Huyghen's work, suggested in 1671 that the length of a pendulum beating seconds be taken as a fixed and easily recoverable standard of length.

After his original suggestion of the "seconds" pendulum, Picard realized that the diurnal motion of the earth would introduce a variable. He reasoned correctly that a pendulum of given length would swing more rapidly at the north and south poles than it would at the equator. He tried to prove this theory but failed. Picard did, however, measure the meridian from Mahoisine to Amiens, deducing the value of one degree as 68.945 miles.

Sir Isaac Newton

Sir Isaac Newton, who spelled out the mechanics of the universe, had no direct interest in metrology as such but he contributed nevertheless. Had he carried his investigation of the nature of light a little farther, he might have anticipated by more than two hundred years the very valuable concept of interferometry.

Newton's fame rests primarily on his statements of the laws of motion and gravitation. Shortly after graduation at Cambridge he invented differential calculus, and his PRINCIPIA was the greatest scientific book published up to that time.

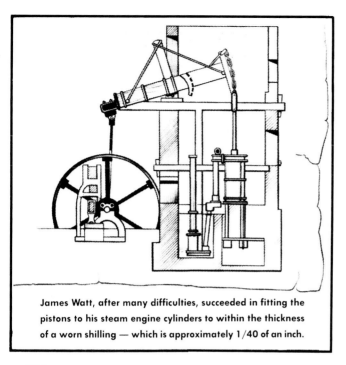

James Watt, after many difficulties, succeeded in fitting the pistons to his steam engine cylinders to within the thickness of a worn shilling — which is approximately 1/40 of an inch.

the eighteenth century

Jacques Cassini

A proposal for a permanent standard of length came in 1718 from Jacques Cassini, head of the Paris Observatory. After measuring the arc of the meridian from Dunkirk to Perpignan, Cassini suggested as a permanent standard of length 1/6000 part of a minute of the great circle of the earth — approximately one third of our present yard.

Early 18th century metrology was by and large a personal matter of the comparatively few persons who had any reason to be concerned with it. There were, of course, the Yard and the Ell of Queen Elizabeth, but these were relatively inaccessible to the individual craftsman or merchant. Manufacturing was still in the cottage-industry stage and each small shop or forge had its own set of standards.

The best examples of early shop standards are the "Polhem Sticks" or Rods used in the early 18th century in Sweden and mentioned by Torsten K. W. Althin in his book C. E. JOHANSSON. These were fixed size

17

gages made of iron, incorporating steps or studs to define several of the dimensions required in the shops where they were used.

Further evidence of the chaos in measurement that characterized the eighteenth century is found on the legend of a map of Tyrol made in 1774. This map has several scales of miles each divided into feet.

One was the "Common German Mile" which was taken as 1/15 of a degree at the equator. This is subdivided into 23,524 "Work Shoes of Vienna" and 22,272 "Work Shoes of Innsbruck."

Another was the "Great German Mile" subdivided into 32,000 "Innsbruck Work Shoes."

Still another was the "Italian Mile" or 1/60 of a degree at the equator. This contained 5,881 Vienna Work Shoes or 5,568 Innsbruck Work Shoes.

The Tempo Increases

The last half of the eighteenth century proved to be a turbulent and eventful period. The American and French revolutions were fought. The British Museum and the Royal Academy were founded. Priestley discovered oxygen. It was the era of Gluck, Haydn, Mozart, and Beethoven. James Watt did his monumental work on the steam engine and Eli Whitney had started to demonstrate the practicability of interchangeable manufacture.

The spinning jenny, the water frame, and power loom ushered in the "Factory System" in England, which was to bring about drastic political and economic changes.

Within the scope of metrology such names as Thomas Jefferson, Bird, Shuckburg, Troughton, and Kater appear. It was in this period, also, that the Metric System was brought into being.

James Watt and the Steam Engine

The operations of James Watt, the famous steam engineer of this period, cast light on the status of manufacturing equipment then available.

Having undertaken the task of improving the Newcomen engine, Watt applied his analytical and inventive mind to the engine's limitations and to the solution of the theoretical problems involved in its improvement. But his problems were not restricted to design. He ran headlong into the serious limitations of metal cutting tools then available.

More specifically, he needed steam cylinders and at the start there were no machines capable of boring a cylinder with accuracy sufficient for his purpose. He got around the difficulty at first by hammering the cylinder into shape over a wooden mandrel.

After nearly four years of work on another cylinder which was bored, rags, cork, and an old felt hat were still needed as packing to keep the steam from leaking excessively around the piston.

It was not until John Wilkinson in 1774 devised a boring bar with a support at its outer end, that reasonably true cylinders could be bored. Watt's partner, Boulton, wrote in 1776: "Mr. Wilkinson has bored us several cylinders almost without error; that of 50" in diameter which we put up at Lipton (or Tipton) does not err the thickness of an old shilling in any part."

Watt coined the term "horsepower." In order to impress prospective buyers with the power of his engine, he found out by experiment how much weight a strong dray horse could lift a distance of one foot in one minute. On that basis, his engine had the power of 40 horses and that proved convincing to his prospects.

Eli Whitney, father of mass production of interchangeable parts was the first to use precision manufacturing in his American gun factory.

birth of interchangeable manufacture

Until the close of the eighteenth century, the only craftsmanship known was the craftsmanship of individuality: that, for instance, which enables a sculptor to chisel a face with such fidelity that the marble becomes recognizable as the image of a certain person.

The individual craftsman made a product in its entirety, fitting each component as he went along. Depending on his training and ability, his products were more or less acceptable, but no two similar products or components were identical. Indeed, there was no particular reason at the time why they should be, so long as manufacturing was limited to very small lots. This, of course, is not the craftsmanship of multiple and precise duplication on which modern industry is founded.

This concept began to be recognized as production volumes increased, as it became evident that economy demanded further division of manufacturing labor, and as the demand for replacement parts began to be a problem.

One of the first artisans to see the economic possibilities of inter-changeable part manufacture was a French gunsmith by the name of LeBlanc. In 1785 Thomas Jefferson, as United States Minister to France, heard about LeBlanc, who had worked out a plan for interchangeable musket parts manufacture 15 years previously. Jefferson was keenly interested and endeavored to bring LeBlanc to the United States but failed.

The first period of the Napoleonic Wars emphasized the imperative need for interchangeable parts. For the first time, very large armies with firearms were put into the field. This brought an unprecedented demand for muskets which craftsmen, working on the old basis, met after a fashion. However, the maintenance of these arms soon became a prob-lem of the first magnitude. Each spare part had to be made and fitted individually — a slow and very expensive operation. At one time the British Government had 200,000 stands of muskets awaiting repair — probably more than were in serviceable condition. It was a problem that had to be solved.

The two essentials for interchangeability are reliable measurements and machine tools. As previously mentioned, there was no uniformity in measurement standards, and machine tools were in their infancy.

Eli Whitney — Father of Mass Production

Eli Whitney, a Yale graduate about 1793, is perhaps best known for having devised the first mechanical cotton gin. Although a financial failure for its inventor and his partner Phineas Miller, the cotton gin was to put the southern cotton industry on its feet economically. It was not, however, Whitney's greatest contribution to American progress.

Whitney recognized the wastefulness of handicraft methods of manufacture just as the Egyptians had done nearly five millenniums be-fore the Christian Era. He also realized that if more than one workman were to contribute to a final product, the work of each must be con-trolled dimensionally in order that all components would assemble when brought together. This, of course, is the essential characteristic of inter-changeable parts manufacturing on which any successful mass produc-tion operation is based.

Whether Whitney knew anything of LeBlanc's ideas is not known. In any event, LeBlanc had only a theory — an unproved theory.

In his effort to manufacture cotton gins on a quantity basis, Whitney initiated the policy of dividing the work into a number of separate operations, each of which was handled by a worker trained for his own particular job.

The idea was sound enough and might have been successful. The trouble was that most of the skilled craftsmen had previously left New England for the fabulous prospects of life in the new Western Reserve. Parts made under Whitney's system by the unskilled apprentices he was able to hire, failed to assemble. Reworking proved costly, as is always the case, so after many set-backs Whitney and his partner closed their cotton gin business in 1797.

The following year Whitney, still convinced of his manufacturing philosophy, wrote to the Secretary of the United States Treasury:

"By the debates in Congress I observe that they are about making some preparations for procuring arms, etc. for the United States . . . I should like to undertake to manufacture ten or fifteen thousand stand of arms."

"I am persuaded that machinery moved by water, adapted to this business, would greatly diminish the labor and facilitate the manufacture of this article. Machines for forging, rolling, floating, boring, grinding, polishing, etc. may all be made use of to advantage."

Whitney proposed to manufacture these arms on his new principle — to make the same parts of different guns as much alike as the successive impressions of a copper plate engraving. Ordnance officers laughed at the idea; his promise of 10,000 stand of arms in two years was preposterous by handicraft methods.

With the help of his friend Thomas Jefferson, Whitney got the government contract in 1798 and began setting up the Whitney Armory at Whitneyville just outside of New Haven. Then, faced with the same obstacles that plagued James Watt, he had to build a plant, all his jigs, fixtures, gages, and most of his machinery — a tremendous undertaking in view of the primitive state of the mechanical arts at that time. Tooling up actually took much longer than anticipated but an extension in delivery time kept Whitney in business.

In 1799 Whitney went to Washington with a box of parts for 10 muskets. Before an audience consisting of President John Adams, Thomas Jefferson and other officials, he assembled the muskets as each of the officials handed him the parts picked up at random from the pile on the table. Whitney thus proved his theory of interchangeable parts manufacture was practicable. Later, with his plant fully tooled, he proved the real economy of his ideas. In 1822 Mr. Calhoun, Secretary of War, said that Whitney's methods were saving the United States $25,000 a year.

When the British decided in 1853 that something should be done to revitalize their Enfield arms plant, a Royal Commission was sent to investigate the American system. In accordance with James Nasmyth's recommendations, the American system was installed in the Royal Armory and American tool builders furnished much of the new equipment needed.

During the period of tooling-up the Armory at Whitneyville, Whitney developed his milling machine. This was also about the time that Roberts in England brought out his hand-driven metal planer.

With the quality and economy of the Whitney musket established, further government contracts contributed to build a prosperous business.

At Whitney's death in 1825, his son Eli II took over the business, and after him the grandson Eli III. In 1888 the entire plant was sold to the Winchester Repeating Arms Co. Whitney, a man of vision and courage, worked always to his motto: "There is nothing worth doing that is not worth doing well."

Cannon Specifications

An interesting sidelight on metal working toward the end of the 18th century, is shown by the tolerances allowed the manufacturer of cannon for the United States Navy.

In 1794 a contract was let for 34 iron cannon to fire a 32 pound shot and 35 more pieces to fire 24 pound shot. These were to be used on the frigates Constitution and Constellation.

The tolerance on bore diameter was plus .10" and minus .05". Holes in the bore could not be more than .225". It is quite apparent why naval engagements of that time had to be fought out at very close range.

the metric system

For more than a hundred years before the meter was legalized, scientific minds had recognized the need for a universal standard of measurement. Preferably a standard based on some natural constant.

The suggestions of Jean Picard and Jacques Cassini have already been mentioned. In addition, there was the proposal of Gabriel Mouton in 1670 to adopt the arc of one minute of a great circle of the earth as the standard.

Sir Humphry Davy suggested the diameter of a glass capillary tube in which water would rise by surface tension to a height just equal to the tube's diameter.

In 1790 Thomas Jefferson, then Secretary of State, in a report to the Congress recommended a standard based on the length of a seconds pendulum. Unlike the pendulums of Picard and Cassini, Jefferson's pendulum was to have a constant cross section throughout — no concentrated weight at the lower end and half again as long as the weighted-end pendulum. Such a pendulum would be about 58-3/4" long. Jefferson further suggested this pendulum be subdivided into five equal parts or feet and each foot be divided into 10 equal parts or inches. This report, like so many since, was merely filed.

Metre Des Archives

The French National Assembly in 1790 appointed a committee to study the several suggestions that had been made for a basic standard of length. Its decision was in favor of a standard that would be one ten-millionth of a quadrant of the earth's meridian.

The geodetic survey which served to establish this length was made from Dunkirk in France to Montjuich in Spain.

Another committee, composed of the members of the National Institute of France and certain foreign deputies, was given the task of drawing up the system of weights and measures and preparing prototypes. This committee produced in 1799 a platinum-iridium end bar known thereafter as the "Metre des Archives." This was to have been the master standard of the world. Its length is on the same order of magnitude as that of the seconds pendulum.

France legalized the Metre des Archives in 1799 and in 1801 made the use of the Metric System compulsory.

The Committee Meter

Under the direction of J. G. Tralle, a deputy from the Helvetic Republic, fifteen iron bars similar to the Metre des Archives were constructed for distribution to the deputies of his committee. One of these which came to be known as "The Committee Meter" was presented by Mr. F. R. Hassler.

When Mr. Hassler came to this country in 1805 he presented the standard to the Philosophical Society of Philadelphia. Later, when he became superintendent of the Coast Survey, he used the Committee Meter as a reference.

France Rejects the Meter

Although the meter became the legal standard, French authorities for a time found it impossible to enforce its use. Practically every French city had its own standards and continued to use them in defiance of the national law. Finally, attempts at enforcement were completely abandoned when Napoleon became First Consul. No further efforts to enforce the law were made until 1837 under Louis Phillippe.

Subsequent to the construction of the "Metre des Archives," discrepancies were discovered in the geodetic survey on which this standard is based. Its length was found to be one part in 5000 shorter than one ten-millionth of the quadrant of a meridian.

Efforts to Universalize the Meter

At the time the metric system was being considered by France, Talleyrand proposed a joint commission of France and England to consider establishing the meter as a universal standard. Had that idea succeeded, subsequent generations of manufacturers would have been saved a great deal of inconvenience.

By 1870 the metric system had been adopted by Holland, Belgium, and Italy. Still, it was far short of being the universal standard that France had hoped it would become.

Holding to that objective nevertheless, France invited the nations to a conference in 1870 to discuss the advisability of constructing new metric standards to supplant those of the Archives. Fifteen nations sent delegates to this conference, including France herself, Austria, Columbia, Ecuador, Great Britain, Greece, Italy, Norway, Peru, Portugal, Russia, Spain, Switzerland, Turkey and the United States. Work, however, was seriously handicapped by the turmoil of the Franco-Prussian War then in progress. Little was accomplished.

A subsequent conference, in 1872, was more successful. It resulted in a decision to reconstruct the basic metric standards to conform in length and weight with those of the Archives. A permanent committee was organized to carry this decision into effect. By 1875, its work was sufficiently complete for another general convention to be called.

The International Bureau Established

At this convention of 1875, a treaty was negotiated whereby a permanent International Bureau of Weights and Measures was established.

A place for the Bureau's headquarters was provided by France at Sevres, a suburb of Paris in the Parc de St. Cloud. The land was designated international territory.

The Bureau under an elected governing committee of 14, no two from the same country, undertook to authenticate the new standards, act as custodian of the International Prototypes, and make comparisons between them and the national standards of other countries.

New International Standards

Thirty-one meter bars and forty kilograms had been constructed by 1889 and approved by the Bureau's governing committee. The bar and kilogram which agreed most closely with their respective counterparts at the Archives were selected as the new International Standards. The remainder were distributed to the nations represented in the Bureau. The United States received Meters No. 21 and 27 together with kilograms No. 4 and 20.

The new meter bar composed of 90% platinum and 10% iridium was made in what is termed the Tresca section, for maximum physical rigidity. This, the International Prototype Meter, is kept in a massive concrete vault, guarded by heavy iron doors three flights of steps below the ground floor of a white stone building in the Parc de St. Cloud.

At each General Conference, held every six years, the delegates descend the steps, open the iron doors and enter the vault to formally inspect the international prototype in its triple case of glass, vulcanized rubber and wood.

The International Prototype Meter, unlike its predecessor of the Archives, is a line standard instead of an end standard. It has three microscopic lines engraved on its web at either end. The distance between the central lines in each group of three under certain conditions defines the meter. These conditions are that the measurement be made at normal atmospheric pressure, the meter bar being at the temperature of melting ice and supported on two rollers one centimeter in diameter and symmetrically placed 572 mm apart. No reference was made to either the Metre des Archives or to the length of the earth's quadrant.

Light Waves

The International Conference of Weights and Measures at its meeting in 1927 adopted a secondary definition of the meter in terms of the wave length of red cadmium radiation, based on the work of A. A. Michelson and E. W. Morley nearly 30 years previously. The length, as thus determined, is 1,553,164.13 wave lengths under specified conditions of temperature, humidity, and atmospheric pressure.

Beginning in 1960, the meter has been defined as 1,650,763.73 wavelengths of orange-red light emitted by electrically excited atoms of Krypton-86 gas. The Krypton lamp is immersed in liquid nitrogen and its light output is used in an interferometer to measure length.

Current Definition of the Meter

The nations of the world, meeting at the General Conference on Weights and Measures in Paris in October, 1983, adopted a new definition for the meter. Based largely on research by the National Bureau of Standards, the new method defines the meter as the distance traveled by light in a vacuum during 1/299,792,458 of a second.

National Bureau of Standards Director, Ernest Ambler, terms the new definition a "real break-through" for measurement science. "It not only allows us to define the meter 10 times more accurately, but also achieves a long-sought goal of using time — our most accurate measurement — to define length."

7
the nineteenth century

By the beginning of the 19th century, such basic machine tools as Wilkinson's boring mill and a screw cutting lathe of sorts had been built in France. The lead screw and change gears had been used in France, but it was the first half of the 19th century that witnessed really great expansion in the machine tool industry. By 1850 practically all the basic machine tools had been developed.

During this period Henry Maudsley developed the engine lathe, the index milling machine and the first screw machine made entirely of metal. Whitworth contributed his end measures and the Whitworth thread form. Eli Whitney built his milling machine; Roberts, his planer; and the principle of the crowned pulley was discovered.

Imperial Standard of Britain Under George

The British were naturally interested in the new Metric System, but not sufficiently so to abandon their traditional Yard. Rankine's verse although penned forty years later, expressed the popular view.

> Some talk of millimeters,
> and some of kilograms
> And some of deciliters
> to measure beer and drams
> But I'm a British Workman,
> too old to go to school
> So by pounds I'll eat,
> and by quarts I'll drink,
> And I'll work by my three-foot rule.

The Elizabethan Yard remained the British standard until four years after George IV took the throne. Then, by an act of Parliament in 1824, all previous laws relating to standards, including Elizabeth's, were repealed. Thereafter, all measures of length were to be based on a standard yard constructed under the direction of the Parliamentary Committee of 1758.

An abstract from that act reads as follows:

SECTION I. Be it enacted... that from and after the first day of May,

29

one thousand eight hundred and twenty-five, the Straight Line or Distance between the Centers of the Two Points in the Gold Studs in the Straight Brass Rod now in the Custody of the Clerk of the House of Commons, whereon the Words and Figures "Standard Yard, 1760" are engraved, shall be and the same is hereby declared to be the Extension called a Yard; and that the same Straight Line or Distance between the Centers of the said Two Points in the said Gold Studs in the said Brass Rod, the Brass being at a temperature of sixty-two Degrees by Fahrenheit's Thermometer, shall be and is hereby denominated the "Imperial Standard Yard."

SECTION III. And whereas it is expedient that the said Standard Yard, if lost, destroyed, defaced, or otherwise injured, should be restored to the same Length by reference to some invariable natural Standard; and whereas it has been ascertained by the Commissioners appointed by His Majesty to inquire into the subject of Weights and Measures, that the Yard hereby declared to be the Imperial Standard Yard, when compared with a Pendulum vibrating Seconds of Mean Time in the Latitude of London in a Vacuum at the Level of the Sea, is in the proportion of Thirty-six Inches to Thirty-nine Inches and one thousand three hundred and ninety-three ten-thousandth Parts of an Inch; Be it therefore enacted and declared, that if at any time hereafter the said Imperial Yard shall be lost or shall be in any Manner destroyed, defaced, or otherwise injured, it shall and may be restored by making a new Standard Yard, bearing the same proportion to such Pendulum as aforesaid, as the said Imperial Standard Yard bears to the Pendulum.

Bird's Yard Bar

It may be of interest to note that this is the first British standard to be designated an "Imperial" standard. It was made by Bird in 1760 using as an unofficial reference a yard measure made in 1742 for the Royal Society which in turn was based on the Elizabethan Standard.

Bird's Imperial Standard with all its legal distinction and care had probably the shortest official life of any national standard — just a few days more than nine and a half years. It was badly damaged by the fire which burned both houses of Parliament in 1834.

When pulled out of the rubble it was found that one of the gold plugs had been melted out — consequently, as a standard it was useless. It seems to have been lost until 1891 when it was again brought to light by a Clerk of the Journals. It was then removed to the residence of the Clerk of the House.

Restoration of the Imperial Standard

After the Parliament fire, it was necessary either to restore or to reproduce the burned standard. The wording of the statute was very explicit about the reproduction procedure but this did not preclude considerable difficulty in its execution.

It seems that errors were discovered with reference to the determination and use of the control pendulum — errors serious enough to make the pendulum impracticable for the purpose.

Fortunately there were some unofficial standards which had been compared with the Imperial Standard before the fire. These included the Shuckburgh Scale, the Yard of the Royal Society and two iron bars A_1 and A_2 belonging to the Ordnance Department.

The Shuckburgh Scale (0-36") was made by Edward Troughton in 1798 and found to agree closely with Bird's Bar. It had also been compared with the pendulum and the meter.

Troughton seems to have been the first to use a microscope for the purpose of precise comparison and transfer of precise measurements.

The actual work of reproduction was begun by Sir Francis Baily. It was Baily who, before his death in 1844, decided on the material of which the new standard was made — copper 16, tin 2-1/2, and zinc 1.

The Rev. R. Sheepshanks took over Baily's task at his death and, from an average of the standards mentioned above, produced "Bronze No. 1." Its graduations are engraved on the polished surfaces of gold plugs depressed to a plane which coincides with the neutral axis of the bar. Depressing the graduated plugs was done to neutralize errors that might result from flexure when comparisons were being made.

Accurate duplicates were made of Bronze No. 1 for official use in Britain and were legalized by Parliament in 1855. In addition, 40 more copies were made for distribution to other governments. One of these Bronze No. 11, was presented to the United States Government in 1856.

In recent years the platinum-iridium bar has been replaced as the primary standard of length by more precise atomic and electro-optic methods.

standards of the united states

Colonial Times

The early standards of weight and measure in what was later to be the United States were all of English origin inasmuch as we started as English colonies.

While the Yard of Queen Elizabeth was theoretically the basis for British length measure, the technique of duplicating a precision standard was rather sketchy in the early days. As a result, the alleged copies of Elizabeth's Yard that came into the several American colonies from time to time lacked a great deal in the matter of precise agreement. Naturally, this confusion became progressively more irritating to the colonists as American culture developed.

Articles of Confederation

The question of uniformity in weights and measures was therefore given consideration in the Articles of Confederation when they were undertaken by a congressional committee in 1776. This document includes the following: "The United States in Congress assembled shall also have the sole and exclusive right and power of regulating the alloy and value of coin struck by their own authority, or by that of the respective States — fixing the standard of weights and measures throughout the United States."

Congress promptly used its authority to regulate the currency but seemed reluctant to do anything but consider the question of national standards of weight and measure.

Washington Urges Action

President Washington, recognizing the necessity, stated in his first message to Congress: "Uniformity in the currency, weights and measures of the United States is an object of great importance, and will, I am persuaded, be duly attended to."

This resulted in a request to Thomas Jefferson, then Secretary of State, to prepare a report outlining the procedure for developing uniform standards.

Jefferson's report contained alternate plans. The first was to unify existing weights and measures. The second was to simplify both weights and measures by decimal subdivision. As has happened so many times since, Congress dallied with this project ineffectively until 1799 in spite of Washington's continued insistence on action.

The Fifth Congress did pass an act requiring the surveyor of each port to examine weights and measures used at the port twice a year and report disagreements to the collector of customs there. In the absence of any standards of comparison, the act was practically meaningless and, in fact, was not enforced for about 30 years after its passage.

Further Congressional attempts were made to deal with the problem in 1817 and 1819, and resulted in a complete report from the then Secretary of State John Quincy Adams to the House of Representatives in 1821. This report suffered the same fate as that made by Jefferson some thirty years before.

Congress Had a Difficult Problem

Perhaps Congress should not be criticized too harshly for its desultory tactics on this issue, which in reality was far from a simple piece of routine legislation. The metric system had met such popular resistance that it had been abandoned. The British system of weights and measures was not wholly in accordance with the miscellaneous standards in use in America, nor was it too well established even in Britain. Would either system survive? No one knew.

The States Act Independently

Without national leadership each of the several states set up its own standards regardless of the actions of other states. The old confusion persisted. The yard, the foot, and the inch were all peculiar to localities and changed at state boundaries.

This was the status of weights and measures when, in 1824, Parliament under George IV established new British Imperial Standards to supersede those of Queen Elizabeth. How much effect this had on Americans, it is hard to say, but it doubtless had some. Britain had now made a serious effort to clear the atmosphere, spell out the rules, and minimize uncertainties with respect to standards.

The First Legal Standard of Weight

In the United States, the law makers could be somewhat casual about the exact length of the inch or yard, but they could not be so informal about the exact amount of gold or silver that went into coins. Money was too important.

The British had a new imperial troy pound and the indication was that it had a degree of permanence. It may, of course, have been just a coincidence, but when Congress, in 1828, passed an act to continue the Mint at Philadelphia, it adopted this new imperial troy pound. An excerpt from the act states: "And be it further enacted, That, for the purpose of securing a due conformity in the weight of coins of the United States — the brass troy pound weight procured by the minister of the United States at London in the year one thousand eight hundred and twenty-seven, for the use of the mint and now in the custody of the Mint at Philadelphia, shall be the standard troy pound of the Mint of the United States, conformably to which the coinage thereof shall be regulated."

This was a brass weight and an exact duplicate of the British imperial troy pound according to Captain Kater who compared the two. This weight became the basis of the avoirdupois pound still used in this country.

It is obvious that even Congress could not ignore the question of length standards forever. Two years after we had acquired the troy pound, legislative machinery was set in motion again for the purpose of acquiring such a standard.

The Treasury Department Takes the Initiative

The Secretary of the Treasury was ordered to report on the weights and measures in use by the principal custom houses. Except for the recently legalized pound, Mr. F. R. Hassler, Superintendent of the Coast Survey who headed the investigation, found himself in the same position as the port surveyors in 1799 when they were faced with the same problem: no length standard with which local measures could be compared.

In this case, the Treasury Department on Hassler's recommendation, chose to comply with the spirit of the order. That left no alternative but to usurp the prerogative of the Congress and establish standards even though they were not official.

These standards were the gallon of 231 cubic inches, the bushel of 2,150.42 cubic inches and a brass scale of 82 inches made by Edward Troughton of London and brought to this country by Hassler. The yard was defined as the distance between the 27th and 63rd inch marks on this Troughton Scale.

Hassler's work was so well received that the House of Representatives passed a resolution in 1836 authorizing the Treasury Department to have copies of its still unofficial standards made for each of the custom houses and for other purposes.

The Office of Weights and Measures

In order to carry out this program, the Office of Weights and Measures was created under the Superintendent of the Coast Survey. By 1850 practically all the states had a set of the Hassler standards.

When the United States received Bronze No. 11 in 1856, it was compared with the Troughton Scale. The latter was found to be .00087" longer than Bronze No. 11.

The Meter Becomes the U.S. Standard

Bronze No. 11 and a second copy of the Imperial Yard received later were considered better standards than the Troughton Scale and therefore replaced the Troughton Scale as the basic reference of the Office of Weights and Measures. They remained our standards, although still unofficial, until 1866 when Congress passed the act legalizing the metric system. This act gave the United States its first and only legal standards of weight and measure.

Excerpts from the act of July 28, 1866 follows:

Be it enacted by the Senate and House of Representatives of the United States of America in Congress assembled, that from and after the passage of this act it shall be lawful throughout the United States of America to employ the weights and measures of the metric system, and no contract or dealing or pleading in any court shall be deemed invalid or liable to objection because the weights or measures expressed or referred to therein are weights or measures of the metric system.

Sec. 2. And be it further enacted, That the tables in the schedule hereto annexed shall be recognized in the construction of contracts and in all legal proceedings as establishing in terms of the weights and measures now in use in the United States the equivalents of the weights and measures expressed therein in terms of the metric system; and said tables may be lawfully used for computing, determining, and expressing in customary weights and measures the weights and measures of the metric system.

The Treasury Department was ordered to provide each state with a set of metric prototypes. This assignment was carried out by the Office of Weights and Measures using the "Committee Meter" and the Arago Kilogram for reference. These remained our official standards until 1893.

Meters No. 21 and No. 27

As previously stated, after the International Bureau of Weights and Measures was established, new International Standards were constructed. The United States, a signatory power, received Meters No. 21 and 27 together with Kilograms No. 4 and 20.

After formal verification in 1893, the Superintendent of Weights and Measures with the authority of the Secretary of the Treasury, decided that the new international prototypes would replace the earlier metric standards for use in the United States. As a matter of fact, the new international prototypes were practically identical in size with their predecessors according to comparisons made at the time.

Current Standards

Kilogram No. 20 remains the official legal standard of mass in the United States, while as mentioned earlier, the meter is now defined in terms of the distance light travels in a vacuum during a precisely measured time interval. The yard is defined legally in terms of the meter.

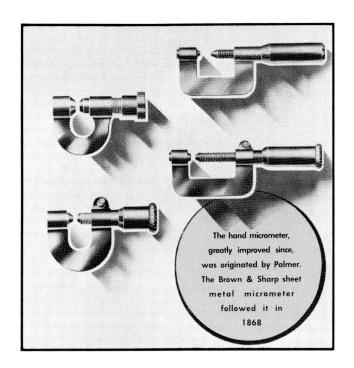

The hand micrometer, greatly improved since, was originated by Palmer. The Brown & Sharp sheet metal micrometer followed it in 1868

precision developments including the micrometer

Henry Maudslay, one of the founders of the machine tool industry, recognized the imperative need for precision in any machine designed to make elements for other machines.

Incidentally Joseph Whitworth, later knighted, and James Nasmyth, both to win renown in that field, were apprentices in Maudslay's organization.

It was Maudslay who built the first screw-cutting lathe entirely of metal in 1800. The critical element of this lathe was a master lead screw. Maudslay's problem then became the production of a precision lead screw. It was somewhat the same as the old question of which came first, the chicken or the egg.

It is true that Besson, a French engineer, had built a screw cutting lathe more than 200 years before Maudslay was born, but it probably did not measure up to Maudslay's ideas of precision.

We are told that it took about ten years of diligent work on Maudslay's part to produce a satisfactory lead screw.

Although Maudslay did not invent it, he did build a screw microm- eter caliper in 1805, for use in his own shop, that was probably the most accurate instrument of that day. He called it "The Lord Chancellor." It was a bench-type instrument (not a hand micrometer) about 16 inches long. The basic scale was graduated in tenths of an inch. The end of the actuating screw had a milled head graduated in 100 divisions, each of which represented a jaw movement of .001".

James Nasmyth remarked at the time, "Not only absolute measure could be obtained by this means, but also the amount of minute differ- ences could be ascertained with a degree of exactness that went quite beyond all the requirements of engineering mechanism; such, for in- stance, as the thousandth part of the inch."

No reference has been found relative to Maudslay's standards of length. Presumably they were derived from the yard of Queen Elizabeth because at that time the Imperial Yard had not yet materialized.

There is no intention to leave the impression that the above are the only achievements of Maudslay. He built his index milling machine in 1829 and other tools. He also built the engine in 1823 for the first steam- driven ship of the Royal Navy — H.M.S. "Lightning."

This was sixteen years after Fulton's steamboat made its trial run, and two years before the Erie Canal was opened.

Sir Joseph Whitworth

Joseph Whitworth, 22 years younger than Maudslay, was doubtless influenced by the older man's reverence for precision and also perhaps by Maudslay's early preoccupation with screw threads.

Ideas of this scope have always been a challenge to men with ambi- tion and integrity.

After his apprenticeship in and about London he set up his own tool shop in Manchester in 1833.

One of his early special interests was the surface plate which his mentor, Maudslay, had introduced. The surface plate has just two impor- tant characteristics — a plane surface and rigidity. Rigidity is not much of a problem but securing a true plane surface is quite another matter.

In a paper presented in 1840 to the British Association in Glasgow he stated, "A true surface, instead of being in common use, is almost unknown." That, of course, was in 1840. And Whitworth referred not only to surface plates but also to the surfaces of engine slide valves, printing press tables, machine tool slides, and other surfaces required to be true.

He described in this paper the method for obtaining a true plane which won general recognition. Starting with three approximately plane surfaces, he arbitrarily chose one as a model, bringing the other two up to conformity with it. Then he brought the second two into conformity with each other. In the final step he brought the arbitrarily chosen model into conformity with the remaining two. The whole process was accomplished by scraping — not by grinding.

By the time Whitworth organized his own shop the yard had been stabilized, at least officially, but the form of screw threads was still pretty much a matter of personal preference. A bolt with its mating nut, once made, were kept tied together until they could be used. It was only an outside chance that a bolt made in one place would mate with a nut made elsewhere.

Whitworth, in 1841, started a personal campaign to bring order out of this chaotic condition by promoting a thread form designed by himself that has ever since been known as the Whitworth Thread. His efforts were reasonably successful in England. It took another twenty years before American industry became sufficiently annoyed by the lack of standardization to do much about it.

Other significant contributions by Whitworth were his end standards, interchangeable gages, and measuring machine.

The Whitworth measuring machine, the most precise instrument of its kind up to that time, was sensitive to a millionth of an inch, its principal elements were a frame of great rigidity, the precision lead screw and the graduated micrometer disc, all of which had previously been known and used. The new idea was his "feeling piece."

Whitworth realized that in dealing with end measures to that unheard of degree of accuracy, the amount of gaging pressure was extremely important and must be controlled; therefore, the feeling piece — a small disc of steel having parallel polished faces. With the feeling piece between the gage jaw and the work part, only sufficient pressure is exerted to keep the feeling piece from dropping out.

Whitworth developed, in 1834, three bars equal in length and, combined, equal to the Imperial Yard. He likewise subdivided the foot into inch end measures and, finally, the inch into sixteenths.

As working gages, Whitworth suggested the now familiar plug and ring gages.

The Micrometer

The principle of the micrometer caliper or the use of the screw thread for precision measurement was discovered by William Gascoigne, a young astronomer of Yorkshire, England, in 1637. The inventor, however, was not concerned with the measurement of mechanical elements and could hardly have foreseen the future possibilities of his discovery. In fact, he made no attempt to patent his device. It took more than two centuries to translate Gascoigne's idea into the machinists tool.

We are told that James Watt used a micrometer which is now on exhibit in London's South Kensington Museum.

The "Lord Chancellor," a bench micrometer, made by Henry Maudslay in 1805 has already been described.

The first patent on a "Screw Caliper" was issued to a French mechanic, Jean Laurent Palmer, in 1848. This was a pocket instrument and the forerunner of our present micrometer. Palmer proceeded to manufacture his device under the name "Systeme Palmer." What success Palmer had in promoting it is not known.

A biography of Joseph R. Brown states that in 1852 he invented and constructed a dividing engine which he then used to construct a vernier caliper reading to thousandths, but nothing more is known about that instrument. It is rather difficult to fit this incident into the story of the micrometer because of what transpired later.

It seems that in 1867 there was trouble between the Bridgeport Brass Co. and the Union Metallic Cartridge Co. about the thickness of sheet brass furnished to the latter. The shipment in question was returned as unacceptable.

Bridgeport rechecked the sheets and found them to meet specifications. The trouble was that the Union Co. also had a gage, but it and the Bridgeport gage differed. Both differed with a third gage brought in to settle the dispute. But all were supposed to be based on the United States Standard for Wire Gages adopted in 1857. It was definitely a situation that called for a remedy.

The superintendent of Bridgeport Brass, Mr. S. R. Wilmot designed a micrometer which measured to thousandths. It was read by a pointer which moved across an engraved spiral having the same pitch as the micrometer screw. Axial lines on the engraved spiral indicated the size of the micrometer opening. What made it difficult to read was that the graduations were so close, there was no room for figures. Nevertheless, Wilmot had six of these micrometers made by Hiram Driggs. He also tried unsuccessfully to interest Brown and Sharpe in their manufacture. Their objection was that the instrument was too complicated to be practicable.

About the same time J. R. Brown and Lucian Sharpe, visiting the Paris Exposition, saw a Palmer Micrometer. Using what they considered the best features of both the Palmer and Wilmot designs, they brought out the Brown and Sharpe Micrometer in 1867. This was the first practical mechanic's micrometer marketed in this country. By 1877 it was well established in our metalworking industry.

early comparators

The fact that the Bureau of Standards has Meter Bar No. 27 and Bronze 11 does not necessarily assure a standard meter or foot in American shops. All national prototype length standards are carefully protected, assiduously guarded and relatively inaccessible. Except for a reliable means of transferring their lengths to available industrial standards these supreme standards would be practically useless.

It has been stated in the STORY OF STANDARDS by John Perry, 1955, that the Office of Weights and Measures which preceded our Bureau of Standards had the Meter Bar for ten years without being able to certify conventional industrial standards because the Office had no facilities for subdividing that meter.

In the very early times, a notched stick or a length of knotted cord could serve as a comparator but as precision grew in importance comparators had to be refined accordingly.

One of the earliest attempts at a precision comparator was made by

Joseph Saxton when he built his Reflecting Comparator. In recognition of its value to science, Saxton was awarded the John Scott Legacy Medal in the year 1837, the same year that the first Elizabeth ascended the British throne.

Saxton's comparator seems to be the first instance of the light beam lever arm being used as a means of amplifying very small displacements for measurement.

The moving components of Saxton's comparator consisted of a delicately pivoted vertical spindle which carried a small mirror, and a sliding bar which served as the instrument's gaging anvil.

A very fine watch chain was wound around the mirror spindle with the other end connected to the sliding bar. Thus, any movement of the sliding bar would exert a tangential pull tending to rotate the mirror spindle.

The reflection in the mirror of a circular scale placed 15 or 20 feet distant gave the desired amplification. At 20 feet this amplification was 3840 to 1; a .001" movement of the gaging anvil would cover 3.84" on the scale.

Whether Whitworth's measuring machine, previously described, preceded or followed Saxton's reflecting comparator is not certain. No direct reference dating the introduction of Whitworth's machine has been found.

We know Whitworth had subdivided the Imperial Yard into precise end measures by 1834. It seems incredible that such a formidable task could have been accomplished without a precision comparator such as his measuring machine.

Later, working with the United States Coast Survey in supplying the several states with length standards, Mr. Saxton designed what came to be known as the Saxton Yard Dividing Comparator.

This device has a brass bed-plate with full length V-shaped ways which carries a free-moving microscope slide. A series of brass posts in the bed-plate, each carrying a conical ended steel screw, serve as stops for the several subdivisions of the meter and the yard. The end stops were set for Bronze No. 11 at 58° F and for the iron meter at 68° F.

One of the first precision bench micrometer or measuring machine was developed about 1878 and shortly thereafter the Rogers-Bond Universal Comparator was constructed by the Pratt and Whitney Company from plans proposed by Professor W. A. Rogers and Mr. George M. Bond.

This comparator is more elaborate, has more refinements, and is more versatile than its predecessors. It is adaptable to both line and end standards and offers a choice of five separate methods of comparison.

Readings are made by 150 power microscopes having micrometer eyepieces graduated in divisions of 1/60,000''. It is said that readings can be interpolated by eye to tenths of a graduation.

The following is an excerpt from the report of the Committee on Standards and Gauges at the annual meeting of the American Society of Mechanical Engineers in New York City, November, 1882. Ambrose Swasey was a member of this committee.

"The completion of the Rogers-Bond Comparator marks a long stride in advance over any method hitherto in use for comparison and subdivision of line-measure standards, combining as it does all the approved methods of former observers with others original with the designers. Comparisons can thus be checked thoroughly by different systems, so that the final results of the series may be relied on as being much nearer absolute accuracy than any hitherto produced."

The first truly precise measuring machine to use end standards was developed by Sir Joseph Whitworth.

screw thread standardization

The standardization of screw threads to achieve interchangeability has been as difficult a problem and perhaps more costly than the establishment of accepted length standards.

As previously mentioned, Sir Joseph Whitworth was the first prominent crusader in the cause of standardization. Starting in 1841 he finally persuaded British industry to accept the Whitworth Thread. However, this thread system was based on the inch, which made it awkward for the metric countries, and consequently left them comparatively unresponsive.

At that time American industry had not progressed far enough to realize the necessity for standardization. It was not until the time of the rapid railroad expansion that American industry began to realize the economic waste of screw thread confusion.

In 1840 America had less than 3,000 miles of rail lines. Ten years later mileage had nearly tripled and by 1860 we had more than 30,000 miles of railroads in operation.

In this expansion, together with the concurrent expansion of all the supporting industries, nuts and bolts became important items. Waste due to confusion had become too costly.

Whitworth's American counterpart proved to be William Sellers of Philadelphia, who, after a careful study òf the situation, drew up a screw thread system which he had reason to believe was superior to Whitworth's. The chief points of difference were the thread angle and the contours of root and crest — changes made in the interest of greater manufacturing economy and more effective inspection but without jeopardizing strength, frictional resistance or wear life.

Mr. Sellers recognizing the magnitude of his task, appealed for support to the Franklin Institute of Philadelphia. Founded in 1824, the Franklin Institute was the oldest institution in the United States dedicated to the study and promotion of the mechanical arts and applied science. The Franklin Institute opened Philadlphia's first high school in 1826.

The Franklin Institute responded favorably, and approximately a year before the close of the Civil War a committee was appointed "to investigate the question of the proper system of screw threads, bolt heads and nuts to be recommended to the Institute for general adoption by American Engineers."

This committee reported its findings December 15, 1864. In the course of its investigation the committee was amazed to discover the very large number of screw thread varieties then in current use. The economic implications were obvious.

In a rather lengthy report the committee recommended the Sellers System. Copies of the report were then forwarded to several branches of industry concerned, the railroads, and the government agencies.

The Navy's Bureau of Steam Engineering adopted the Sellers system in 1868, the Pennsylvania Railroad in 1869, the Erie Railroad in 1874. It was also adopted by the Master Mechanics Association, the Master Car Builders Association, and others.

Thus the Sellers system came to be the American Standard with benefits for American industry comparable with those British industry derived from the Whitworth system.

Both countries got along reasonably well until the outbreak of the First World War. Then, suddenly, American, British, and French industries were faced with a common production task but with five different screw thread systems. These were: American Standard, S.A.E., British Standard Whitworth, the British Standard Fine, and the Metric Standard. In addition, the Metric Standard had several variations. It is needless to say that the cost in delays, dollars, and lives was serious. However, the pressure of the conflict left no opportunity to remedy the situation.

At the close of the war, an attempt to reconcile British-American differences proved fruitless.

In 1926 a British mission to the United States proposed a compromise of 57-1/2 degrees between the Whitworth 55 degree thread angle and the American 60 degree angle. This too failed, because we insisted on the 60 degree angle. The problem remained unsolved as time drew closer to another emergency.

World War II caught the industry of both counties still unprepared for effective cooperation in the matter of screw threads. Again the costly delays in turning out urgently needed aircraft engines and ordnance. But again the pressure of war postponed any effort to correct the difficulty.

It wasn't until December of 1943 that the problem of unification was attacked again, this time by a conference in New York. This was followed by two conferences in London in the summer of 1944 and a final conference in Ottawa in September of 1945. The result was agreement on the 60 degree thread angle and a compromise on root and crest contours.

Group conferences of American, British, and Canadian delegates completed formulas for computing tolerances and allowances late in 1948. On November 18th of that year a Declaration of Accord was signed by the representatives of the three countries and our present Unified Screw Thread Standards became a reality at least for the United States and the British Commonwealth.

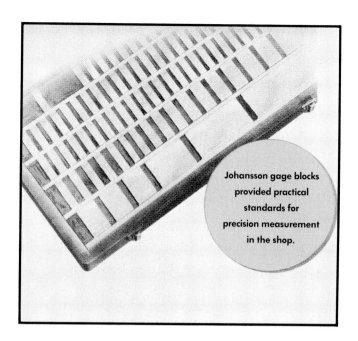

Johansson gage blocks provided practical standards for precision measurement in the shop.

precision gage blocks

The man who did more than any of his predecessors to bring precision measurement directly into the machine shop was Carl Edward Johansson. When he conceived his gage block idea, the tool room had not yet evolved.

In 1887, at the age of 23, Johansson started his apprenticeship in Carl Gustaf's Rifle Factory at Eskilstuna. This organization supplied the Swedish army with rifles. The very purpose of such a product made its reliability imperative; this, in turn, required precision manufacture. Thus it was quite natural for the young apprentice to become precision conscious.

The precision of that day, however, left much to be desired according to modern standards. The control measuring instruments then in the Rifle Factory consisted of snap gages, sliding calipers, and one micrometer reading to .01 mm. The manufacturing gages were steel blocks, one for each dimension. Although the idea of tolerances had been recognized, none were shown on working drawings.

When the Swedish government decided to adopt a magazine rifle, the manufacturing problem was further complicated by a far greater number of precise component parts.

An order for these magazine rifles was placed with the Mauser-Werke, a German firm. The contract provided that the new rifles were to be inspected by a commission from the Eskilstuna plant, and that this commission be given sufficient production information to permit further production to be carried on at Eskilstuna. Johansson was a member of this commission, which went to Germany in 1894.

The task of producing individual gage blocks in the customary way for the many critical dimensions of the new Mauser appalled Johansson. Surely there must be a more effective way to control dimensions. Then his great idea occurred to him: a set of blocks increasing in uniform size increments which could be used singly or in combination to equal any manufacturing dimension encountered.

On his return to Sweden in 1896, Johansson had completed his computation of block sizes for all dimensions in increments of .01 mm from .01 mm to 201 mm or a total of 20,000 different dimensions. This set contained 102 blocks in three series.

There remained, however, the more formidable problems of actual production with the limited equipment and standards then available to him. Besides having to be accurately sized, opposite faces of the blocks had to be parallel and finished to a much higher degree of smoothness than was customary on commercial products. It was further realized that unless the blocks were stabilized they would grow with age and thus lose their accuracy.

At first the question of a basic reference standard was not serious because the initial set of blocks was made for use in the Rifle Factory, which had its own individual length standard. Individual, because it did not necessarily conform with others in the neighborhood. It had been only 9 years since Sweden adopted the Metric System and the transition was still in progress.

Johansson had access to the Brown & Sharpe micrometers used at the Rifle Factory but he recognized their limitations when applied to the problem then at hand. There could be a shadow of doubt whenever the screw thread was used to arbitrate precision measurements, but he had no alternative.

Like Whitworth, he sought to eliminate variations in gaging pressure but in a different manner. Instead of using the conventional thimble Johansson mounted a much larger graduated drum on the micrometer barrel. A cord wound around the drum carried a weight which exerted a constant tangential force on the drum and thus kept gaging pressure constant.

Johansson had the utmost faith in his basic idea but lacked the funds to launch its full scale development as an independent business, so gage block manufacture was started on a part-time basis. Preliminary work on the blocks was done by the Rifle Factory under contract. All finishing was done at first in Johansson's home work shop with improvised equipment and during times when he was not at work in the Rifle Factory.

The first set of blocks, having an accuracy said to be .001 mm was turned over to the Rifle Factory during the year 1896 and immediately put into service. Johansson proceeded with this part time business development until 1914 when he resigned his position as armourer at the factory and thereafter devoted all his time to gage blocks.

There was considerable difficulty at first in obtaining a Swedish patent on gage blocks but the patent was finally issued in January of 1904 with priority allowed to 1901. The British patent was issued in 1902.

Another idea developed and patented (1907) by Johansson was what he termed "progressive tolerances." Prior to that it had been customary to use a bilateral constant tolerance in making fixed size gages, regardless of their nominal size: in other words, the same tolerance for a 10 mm gage as for a meter gage.

As long as end measures such as gage blocks are used singly the bilateral constant tolerance concept is tenable, but when used in multiple there can be a considerable discrepancy in the aggregate length depending on the number of blocks and whether the individual tolerances are plus or minus.

Johansson advocated the principle of using graduated tolerances based on the lengths of the blocks. The smaller the block, the smaller the tolerance. For his own work he adopted a tolerance coefficient of .0001 of the block length. This corresponded closely with the coefficient of thermal expansion of the steel he used to manufacture the blocks.

By 1907 Johansson block sets began to be recognized by American industry. Henry M. Leland of Cadillac was the first automobile manufacturer to have a set. The United States War Department acquired thirty sets in 1915.

Without detracting from Johansson's important achievement, it must be stated that the indicating shop comparator was necessary to give the gage block concept its full effectiveness and flexibility. The shop comparator is the only practical means of bridging block increments.

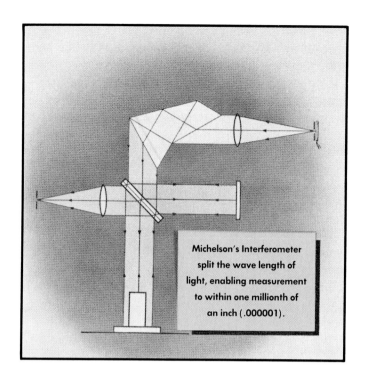

Michelson's Interferometer
split the wave length of
light, enabling measurement
to within one millionth of
an inch (.000001).

time: a new standard

One of metrology's most valuable instruments was developed primarily to help solve a scientific problem rather distantly related to metrology. This instrument is the interferometer; its inventor, the eminent scientist Albert Abraham Michelson.

As with most human progress, the work of the individual begins where his predecessors left off and is continued by his successors. This story really starts with Galileo and it is yet unfinished.

The genesis of the interferometer is that very elusive scientific phenomenon, radiation. What is the ultimate speed at which light can travel? This question is basic to the universal theory of electricity and magnetism and to the theory of relativity.

It has intrigued scientists as far back as Galileo, who tried ineffectually to determine the speed of light with a hand lantern. Ole Roemer, a Danish astronomer in the 17th century, concluded that it took 1000 seconds for light to traverse the diameter of the earth's orbit.

The first attempt at an accurate laboratory measurement was that of Armand Hippolyte Louis Fizeau in 1849. He was followed by more than a score of scientists using a variety of approaches.

Before 1880 Michelson became interested in the problem of light velocity and began work in that field. While a professor at the Case School of Applied Science, Cleveland, Ohio, he undertook to determine what effect, if any, the earth's motion had on the observed velocity of light. While working on this project in 1887, he contrived his interferometer primarily to aid him with the problem then at hand.

We know that Michelson had an interest in metrology inasmuch as he was made a member of the Bureau International des Poids et Mesures in 1882. It seems quite natural, therefore, that he would be quick to see the application of the interferometer to the precision measurement of such objects as gages and mechanical components. Thus it was that light waves entered the realm of metrology and were used by Michelson to measure the International Meter Bar in 1892, with the red band of cadmium as a light source. By this measurement he determined the meter bar to be equivalent to 1,533,164.13 wave lengths of red cadmium light at 760 mm atmospheric pressure. The wave length of that red band of cadmium is .00002534838828 inches.

The interferometer incorporates the previous progress made by many scientists, the most outstanding being Sir Isaac Newton, Christiaan Huyghens, and Thomas Young.

It was Newton who developed the spectrum theory, Huyghens who formulated the wave theory of light, and Young who explained the phenomenon of light wave interference when two or more waves are superimposed.

A continuous sine curve may be taken to represent the wave motion of monochromatic light. This curve had periodic crests with intermediate troughs. If a second sine curve, the crests and troughs of which coincide with those of the first curve, is superimposed on the first, the height and depth of crests and troughs are increased. If, however, the crests of one wave coincide with the troughs of the other, each wave tends to cancel the other. At intervals of one half wave length, wave motion is cancelled completely. When viewed, these points of complete cancellation appear as dark bands or "fringes."

Knowing the wave length of a monochromatic light and being able to count the interference fringes, give us our most valuable standard of measurement.

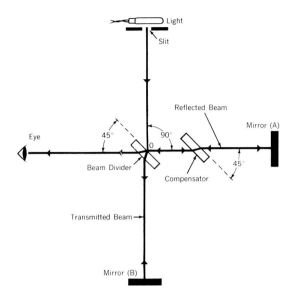

The scheme of Michelson's interferometer is shown above. Monochromatic light such as red cadmium, passing through the light slit, strikes the beam divider at an angle of 45°

The Beam Divider is a transparent plate the sides of which are both flat and parallel. It is silvered in such a manner that part of the light reaching it is reflected toward mirror (A) and part transmitted toward mirror (B). The intensity of the reflected beam is approximately equal to that of the transmitted beam.

The surfaces of both mirrors are normal (perpendicular) to the light beams which strike them.

Assume for a moment that the compensator does not exist. Then the transmitted beam is reflected by mirror "B" and again by the beam divider to the eye. The reflected beam is again reflected by mirror "A" and transmitted by the beam divider to the eye.

Although mirrors "A" and "B" may be equidistant from the point of incidence "O" at the beam divider, the distances traveled by the two beams in reaching the eye are not quite equal. The transmitted beam has to pass through the beam divider plate three times whereas the reflected beam passes through but once. The compensator, a transparent plate with flat parallel sides, is inserted in the optical system to keep the distances traveled by the two beams in balance.

With a balanced optical system, there will be no light wave interference at the eye but a movement of either mirror will change the length of its respective beam and throw that beam out of phase with the other beam to cause interference fringes. By counting these fringes, it is possible to measure the amount of mirror displacement. The amount by which the two waves are "out of phase" due to mirror displacement can be determined to one thousandth of a wave length. For red cadmium this amounts to .00000002534838828 inches.

The light interference principle was also utilized by Fabry and Perot who developed a very simple interferometer. This instrument utilized two flat glass plates from one to five centimeters apart with their surfaces parallel.

The inner surfaces of these plates are silvered so as to reflect most but not all the light which strikes them. Thus, when monochromatic light is beamed into the instrument, that portion which is transmitted by the first plate is reflected back and forth between the plates. On each incidence with the second plate some of the light passes through that plate and may be observed. The air between the plates produces the interference.

Further refinements have been made, culminating in modern instruments such as the Koesters Interferometer, which will be discussed in a later chapter.

Over a period of about 50 years since Michelson measured the International Meter Bar, eight additional observations have been made with the interferometer and a red cadmium light source.

Comparison of the nine results seems to indicate no apparent change in the length of this supreme standard. In spite of this, the evidence thus far cannot be taken as proof that it will always remain stable.

The average of the nine observations is found to be 6438.4696 angstroms. An angstrom is one hundred-millionth of a centimeter or one ten-thousandth of a micron.

One of Michelson's problems was the difficulty of producing monochromatic light in order to attain the desired sharpness of the spectral lines with well defined fringes. He started by using the yellow radiation of sodium only to discard it for the green band of natural mercury which he though would be better. He soon discovered, however, that mercury was far too complex a substance for his purpose. He finally chose the red band of cadmium as the most satisfactory source available at that time.

With the advent of nuclear science, natural mercury was found to be a mixture of seven isotopes with atomic weights 196, 198, 199, 200, 201, 202, and 204. Each has its own spectral line. The 16 components of the green radiation cover a spectral range of more than half an angstrom so it is not hard to understand Michelson's rejection of natural mercury as a light source.

Cadmium is still very useful. In fact, the red radiation of cadmium under prescribed conditions is accepted as an alternate means of defining the length of the International Meter Bar. Nevertheless, cadmium does have its limitations as an interferometric light source. Chief among these is that it is necessary to heat the cadmium tube to approximately 300° C which tends to make the spectral lines fuzzy.

About 50 years ago science set about finding the ultimate in a light source and returned to mercury as the starting point, fully aware that natural mercury was not the goal.

Mercury does have inherent advantages found nowhere else. The green line of mercury is far more actinic to the human eye than the red of cadmium. Furthermore, mercury requires less than half the temperature to attain the necessary radiation. Consequently, the spectral lines of mercury are far more distinct than those of cadmium.

The problem was to isolate an isotope of the complex natural mercury, preferably one having an even-numbered atomic weight. The even-numbered isotopes have no appreciable atomic spin which tends to blur spectral lines. Mercury 198 was selected.

From work done at the University of California it was learned that by bombarding pure gold with neutrons in an atomic pile it could be transmuted to mercury 198 as an end product. Thus the United States Bureau of Standards purchased 40 ounces of pure gold and sent it to Oak Ridge for processing.

In 1948 Dr. Edward V. Condon, Chief of the Bureau, told the Paris Conference on Weights and Measures that the task of producing mercury 198 had been completed and that using this as a light source with an interferometer, measurements could be made to one part in 100 million.

The simplest device for utilizing light wave interference for precision measurement is the optical flat. The optical flat is a disc up to 10 inches in diameter, made usually of clear fuzed quartz, the latter because of its low coefficient of expansion. The surfaces are flat to one millionth of an inch.

The optical flat is used to detect errors in flatness of a precision part and also as a comparator to measure its size.

Light wave interference is produced by the conflict of the light reflected from the lower surface of the flat with that reflected from the upper contact surface of the object being checked. Monochromatic light is used.

To check surface irregularities, for instance, of a gage block surface, the flat is placed against the surface, usually at a slight angle to form an air wedge between flat and block. If the interference fringes are straight and parallel the block surface is flat. If they are parallel and curved, the surface is either convex or concave. If they are irregular, the surface irregularities are thus indicated.

By interposing a part and a standard between two optical flats the size of the part is compared with that of the standard. By measuring the interference fringes all of the above measurements are both quantative as well as qualitative.

Gaging auto engine blocks in the production line

Sheffield Precisionaire checks all cylinder bores
at four points each simultaneously; indicates
piston classification and provides means of
stamping date on each bore. Out of round
and taper are also checked.

||4||
early twentieth century metrology

By the end of the nineteenth century the American machine tool industry
had been firmly established and was growing vigorously with Cincinnati
as its capital. Machine tool progress and the concurrent railroad expansion had provided the strongest stimuli to metrological development
during the last half of the nineteenth century. Its basic theory had been
established, and the rewards for further refinement were becoming increasingly attractive.

The twentieth century did not usher in a new era in metrology, but
almost from the start it provided a strong incentive for progress.

On New Year's day of 1900 William C. Browning of Browning King &
Company said: "In nearly fifty years of business experience I don't believe I ever saw a time when prospects were so bright." Then we had no

aircraft, no radios, no toolrooms, no high speed steel — not even income taxes. The Klondike gold rush was on; oil had been found in California; the telephone was going across country. We had about 8,000 automobiles in the country but no automotive industry.

Johansson blocks had not made their appearance as yet on this side of the Atlantic. Maximum precision in the shop depended on the micrometer. The United States was, in fact, the world's principal source for micrometers at that time.

Manufacturing tolerances had not yet been reduced to .001" for two reasons. Such close tolerances were not required, nor had machine tools reached the degree of precision which would have permitted .001" tolerances. Tolerances to thousandths didn't come into general use until about 1910.

In this country the Office of Standard Weights and Measures was the legal custodian of our national standards but not particularly active in promoting metrology.

Great Britain still relied on the measuring machine and fixed size gages produced by Sir Joseph Whitworth together with American-made micrometers. Actually, close tolerance work was done by highly skilled craftsmen who relied more on the feel of a fit than on any measuring instruments.

Developments in the first half of the twentieth century that had the greatest effect in promoting the importance of metrology were the birth of the automotive industry, the application of mass-production practices, and global war. Metrology was inherently the essence for success in each: metrology together with its blood brother, the machine tool.

The automotive industry, the most dynamic industry the world has ever known, is a product of the twentieth century, but it is difficult to fix its exact birthday.

Frank Duryea in 1893 started building a single cylinder, 4 horsepower, buggy type vehicle in New England. The Detroit Automobile Company which later became Cadillac was started in 1899. The Henry Ford Automobile Company was formed in Detroit in 1901. The Ford Motor Company was incorporated in 1903. W. C. Durant organized General Motors Corporation in 1908. David Buick sold his first car in 1904. The Society of Automobile Engineers was launched in 1905. By that time national annual production of automotive vehicles had reached 25,000.

Duryea was probably the first to freeze a motor car design for subsequent production. Durant pioneered assembly line technique while he was still manufacturing carriages. He formulated the policy of buying component parts rather than manufacturing them in his own plant. Each of his suppliers thus developed his own embryo of mass-production of a specialty which thus could be more effectively and more economically made. From a management standpoint, this practice also relieved Durant of the hazard of carrying a large inventory on his own books.

Mass-production in its current sense began to develop after the first endless chain conveyor was installed at the Highland Park Plant of the Ford Motor Company in 1911. Ford's Charles E. Sorensen is credited with the introduction of the power-driven conveyor assembly line which is basic to modern mass-production.

united states national bureau of standards

"The basic and primary standards (length, mass, and time) are the principal responsibility of the National Bureau of Standards." These were the words, except those in parentheses, of Dr. Allen V. Astin in his address at the dedication of the Eli Whitney Metrology Laboratory of the Sheffield Corporation in Dayton, Ohio, February 17, 1956.

However, custody of our national prototype standards is by no means the Bureau's only responsibility today. The other activities will be discussed later.

While the Bureau wasn't established until 1901, its progenitor, the Office of Standard Weights and Measures, had then served as custodian of standards for a period of 63 years.

In a previous chapter we discussed the confusion over weights and measures that plagued this country in its early years, and the unsuccessful efforts of Washington and Jefferson to prod Congress into action which would give the country uniform standards of length and weight.

While Congress delayed, the need for standardization became more urgent. Finally, in 1830 during Jackson's first presidential term, the Senate directed the Secretary of the Treasury to make a comparison of the haphazard lots of weights and measures then in use by the principal customhouses. Hassler's work in compliance with that order has been discussed.

Six long years later, in 1836 at about the time of the massacre at the Alamo, Congress again went into action, ordering a set of Hassler's unofficial standards to be delivered to each of the States. At that time the only standard that had been duly legalized by Congress was the troy pound used by the Philadelphia mint to regulate coinage.

While the act of 1836 did not specifically legalize the Hassler standards, it did bring about a uniformity in the weights and measures used in the custom service and thus, in practice, by the country at large.

Another joint Congressional resolution in 1838 directed the Treasury to furnish balances to each of the States.

There might be some question as to why these tasks were assigned to the Treasury Department. At that time there were only four Government Departments — State, Treasury, War, and Navy. Of these, the Treasury was the most logical, since as it was already concerned with coinage and it possessed, in the troy pound, the only legal standard we had.

It was also quite logical for the Secretary of the Treasury to set up an organization for administering the acts of 1836 and 1838. Thus was created the Office of Standard Weights and Measures which was placed under the direction of the superintendent of the Coast Survey. The latter group became the Coast and Geodetic Survey in 1878.

While discussing the executive departments of the government, it may be interesting to note that the Department of Commerce and Labor was not organized until February 14, 1903, approximately two years after the National Bureau of Standards continued the work of the Office of Standard Weights and Measures. Ten years later, in 1913, the Department of Commerce and Labor was divided, resulting in the Department of Commerce and the Department of Labor. Today the National Bureau of Standards is an agency of the Department of Commerce.

A leading figure who served 21 years with the former Office of Standard Weights and Measures and who had much to do with the orientation of the Metrology Division of the newly established Bureau was the late Louis A. Fischer. An eminent scientist and a dedicated metrologist, he did much to bring about a better understanding of the role metrology was to play in the years ahead. It was Fischer who inaugurated the Annual Conference on Weights and Measures, the first of which was held in 1905. These conferences, attended by state and local officers charged with the control of weights and measures, have done much to propagate good metrological practice. During World War I Fischer was in charge of all gaging for the War Department.

The ramifications of today's Bureau would bewilder a nineteenth century observer familiar only with the early Office of Standard Weights and Measures.

The act of Congress establishing the Bureau outlined its functions as the development, construction, custody, and maintenance of reference and working standards; and their comparison, improvement, and application in science, engineering, industry, and commerce.

To the unimaginative congressman of half a century ago, such verbiage doubtless seemed sufficiently inclusive to launch a small organization such as the Bureau. After all, there were only fourteen people in this organization at the time.

These lawmakers could not have been expected to realize the

magnitude of the fundamental idea they were dealing with — or its allure for such farsighted men as Fischer, Dr. Condon, Dr. Astin. Today the Bureau is the country's chief physical research laboratory and its supreme arbiter in the field of physical science. From a payroll of 14 persons in 1901, its staff has grown to nearly 3000. Of these, about 40 per cent are professional scientists.

The Bureau spreads out over a 68 acre "campus" in northwest Washington. Its buildings house millions of dollars' worth of the finest scientific instruments and other equipment.

Besides this headquarters installation, the Bureau has laboratories in California and Colorado, twelve domestic stations from coast to coast, and seven overseas stations from the arctic to the tropics.

The scope of the Bureau's operations is indicated by its plan of organization which includes thirteen divisions:

Applied Mathematics; Atomic and Radiation Physics; Building Technology; Chemistry; Electricity; Electronics; Heat and Power; Mechanics; Metallurgy; Mineral Products; Missile Development; Optics and Metrology; Ordnance Development; Organic and Fibrous Materials; Radio.

The Bureau's many scientific activities include:

Fundamental research in the basic properties of matter;

Applied research in the development of new processes, materials and devices;

Developments involving measurement standards, instrumentation and testing practice;

Calibration of instruments; preparation of standard samples for measurements; development of commodity specifications and commodity testing for the Federal Government; technical advice to governmental agencies ;

Compilation and publication of scientific and technical information; production of special materials for the Federal Government; and operation of special installations and services.

The Bureau serves the public directly by furnishing standard samples of materials, testing materials and equipment — and also by calibrating instruments and standards of measurement where sufficiently precise calibration is not elsewhere available.

Under a Research Associate arrangement, Bureau personnel carry on approved research projects requested by private organizations which pay the salaries of those involved. The results of such work become public property and are published.

Some of the Bureau's noteworthy achievements have been in fields of atomic energy, guided missiles, radio propagation, surgical apparatus, panoramic X-ray equipment, and monochromatic light. The Meggers-Mercury 198 lamp, recognized as the best in interferometry, was developed by the Bureau.

the dial indicator

The familiar dial indicator is a legacy from the 19th century watchmakers of New England, developed primarily as a watchmaker's gage. Its broad usefulness to industry in general was not recognized until later.

It is possible at this time, only to speculate on the motivation behind its development. It is readily understandable that the watchmakers, by the nature of their product, were concerned with precision measurement. But the micrometer had been available for more than a decade before the appearance of the dial indicator. The natural conclusion might be that the technical mind then, as now, was constantly striving for means to improve the precision and thereby the quality of manufactured products.

The records of the United States Patent Office show that on May 15, 1883, a patent specification was filed by John Logan of Waltham, Massachusetts, for what we call a dial indicator. He referred to it as "an Improvement in Gages."

In outward appearance this instrument didn't differ much from present indicators but its movement was quite different.

Instead of the now familiar rack and pinion, Logan used a fine Swiss watch chain to transmit the motion of the gaging spindle to the indicating pointer. This chain was wound around a drum, or arbor, which carried the indicating pointer. One end of the chain was fastened to the gaging spindle, the other to the drum. Amplification depended on the diameter of the drum and the length of the indicating pointer.

The practical limitation on the amount of amplification by this method was probably the reason that Logan later switched from the chain movement to a rack and pinion mechanism.

One of Logan's associates was Frank E. Randall, an inventor who learned watchmaking at the E. Howard Watch Company of Boston. Randall, recognizing more fully the broader market for the dial indicator, bought the Logan patents in 1896. In partnership with Francis G. Stickney, he undertook the manufacture and marketing of dial indicators to industry at large. Shortly thereafter, B. C. Ames entered the field, also with a gear-type indicator.

Felix Auerbach, writing of the Zeiss Works and the Carl Zeiss Stiftung in Jena, indicates that German industry, too, was searching for new measuring instruments of greater precision, and for the same reasons.

In 1890 Professor Ernst Abbe established the measuring instrument department of the Zeiss Works. By 1904 this organization had developed a number of instruments for general market consumption. Among them was a dial indicator.

the reed mechanism

During the second decade of the 20th century, industrial leaders, especially those in the young automotive industry, were beginning to appreciate the value of tolerances closer than those for which fixed size gages were suitable. William Bagley, chief inspector for Studebaker, was among the first to advocate replacing these fixed size gages with instrument gages for mass production operations.

Without precision indicating comparators, the full precision potential of the gage block standards introduced by Carl Johansson could not be realized. Nor could parts be classified for selective assembly. Because of the imprecise character of many machine tools of that day, selective assembly was about the only way to achieve the precision fits desired.

The chief obstacle to such progressive concepts was that no practical precision comparator adaptable to mass-production inspection was available. This does not mean that there were no precision comparators. Some have already been mentioned, but they were laboratory instruments requiring a high degree of skill and considerable time to operate. They were far too slow for automotive inspection.

The idea chiefly responsible for circumventing this impasse and opening the way for wide-spread instrument gaging in production was the principle of the reed mechanism.

The reed mechanism is an ingeniously simple mechanical device for amplifying small displacements, in this case the displacement of the gaging spindle. Essentially it consists of two steel blocks and four reeds, the latter made of flexible strips of spring steel.

The blocks, separated slightly, are connected by two horizontal reeds. One block is anchored to the gage head. The other, which carries the gaging spindle, is free to move vertically. The two remaining reeds are solidly fastened to the top inside faces of the blocks, one to each block. These project vertically upward and are joined at their upper ends.

Displacement of the floating block causes the horizontal reeds to flex and the connected ends of the vertical reeds to sweep through an arc, amplified by a pointer and further by an optical system.

The idea of the reed mechanism was conceived by two metrologists, independently but not concurrently. The first was Mr. E. Mark Eden, who developed the idea while he was a member of the staff of the Metrology Division of the National Physical Laboratory of England in 1918. The second was an American. Those attending a gage manufacturers' meeting at Chicago in 1927 were courteously invited to visit the Western Electric plant and look over that company's inspection facilities. Although no especial attention was drawn to it, the display there included an instrument incorporating the reed principle. It had been developed by Mr. Arthur Schoof, a Western Electric Engineer who apparently was quite unaware of the previous work of Mr. Eden.

Among the visitors that day at Western Electric, the only ones who apparently grasped the significance of the reed principle were Mr. C. H. Reynolds and Mr. Charles E. Watterson representing the then Sheffield Machine & Tool Co. They recognized the great potential of this sensitive, frictionless amplifying device as the basis for a new line of comparators which could be used in the shop for fast precision inspection by workers who had no special skill in that area.

The Sheffield Machine & Tool Co. started negotiations with Western Electric for a license to use the reed principle. This was granted in 1929.

The first commercial comparator to incorporate the reed principle was Sheffield's "Electrigage." This instrument showed instantly by light signals whether the part being checked was within tolerance, larger than the maximum tolerance limit, or smaller than the minimum limit.

By 1930 a second comparator known as the Sheffield "Visual Gage" was introduced. This was an indicating comparator utilizing the friction-less reed mechanism together with a weightless light beam lever arm for amplification, and capable of classifying parts for selective assembly.

The Ford Motor Co. was the first automotive manufacturer to use the "Visual Gage" for close limit production inspection. That was in 1930.

||⑧
air gaging

Few ideas have exerted the impact on industrial metrology that pneumatic gaging has. It is one of the spectacular developments of this century, making available the higher amplifications to deal with constantly shrinking manufacturing tolerances and the gaging speed demanded by mass-production operations. It opened the way for multiple and automatic gaging. In short, it has proved an invaluable aid to the rapid progress of modern precision manufacturing since 1940.

Basic Principles

According to historical information, the idea of using a fluid as a gaging medium stems probably from the thinking of Cruikshank and Fairweather. As early as 1917 they suggested the relationship of fluid pressure and nozzle area as the basis of measurement and regulation in the field of paper manufacturing.

Interest in fluids as a means of measurement seemed to spring up spontaneously on both sides of the Atlantic. A United States patent on an air gage was issued to Harrington in 1922. At about the same time, French engineers took up the idea, and their contemporary developments are described in United States patents issued to Mennesson.

A. S. Cachemaille in 1923 announced a method by which the longitudinal vibrations of a dynamo shaft were measured by the flow of gas and water vapor. A similar fluid flow application was made by Guy in England just prior to Cachemaille's.

Western Electric used fluid flow in determining the flatness of telephone receiver discs. Rifle barrels were gaged by the leakage of fluid under pressure between the bore and a master plug.

The first application of air gaging principles in the automotive industry was the determination of carburetor jet area by the Societe Anomyme de Material Automobile (Solex).

Dimensional Air Gages

Although the early work in this field was in the investigation of such characteristics as flatness and area, the experience thus gained prepared the way for the dimensional air gage.

The dimensional air gage is essentially a comparator which utilizes the effect of small dimensional changes on metered air in the gaging circuit. It is based on the fact that the free flow of compressed air through an open orifice is restricted when an obstruction is brought close to it. Such an obstruction reduces the velocity of flow and at the same time raises the pressure in the circuit behind the orifice. The closer the obstruction is to the orifice, within certain limits, the more pronounced are these effects.

In the case of the air gage, the orifice is represented by the jet or jets in the air gage tooling. The obstruction is the surface of the work part being gaged.

By metering either change in back-pressure in the pneumatic circuit or change in its velocity by flow, the clearance between the jets in the air gage tooling and the adjacent work part surface is determined.

Whether the designers of the first commercial dimensional air gage realized their purpose could be accomplished by metering either back-pressure or flow velocity, is not known. No practical velocity metering device had yet been developed.

The first dimensional air gage to be marketed was a back-pressure gage. Solex introduced it in 1926.

Back-pressure in this first Solex gage was metered by means of a water column manometer. Since then back-pressure metering has been accomplished in several ways — one was a pneumatic transducer developed by Britain's National Physical Laboratory. Another was the use of bellows and a third was the familiar Bourdon tube. Deformations of the latter two devices are amplified by a rack, pinion, and pointer assembly similar to that of a dial indicator.

Solex Circuit

Compressed air from a reducing valve enters the gage circuit through a set of restrictions in the outer chamber, which regulate the volume of flow. Pressure stabilization is accomplished by means of an open-end dip-tube immersed to a predetermined depth in a water chamber. Since excess air can escape to the atmosphere through the bottom of the dip-tube, circuit pressure is governed by the hydraulic head from the bottom of the tube to the water surface.

The air at this governed pressure passes through a control jet to an intermediate chamber. This chamber has two outlets, one to the manometer and the other to the gage tooling. Differences in back-pressure originating at the tooling jets are read on a graduated scale behind the manometer column.

Three Dimensional Gage

What is considered to be the first air gage widely marketed in the United States was brought out in 1935 by the Sheffield Gage Corporation for the purpose of exploring the fitness of flat and cylindrical surfaces in three dimensions simultaneously.

The operating principle was the metering of pressure loss between the work part surface and that of a master.

These gages were used to inspect tubing, hydraulic cylinders, and other components required to hold pressure.

As the possibilities of pneumatic gaging became more apparent, more gagemakers became interested, and variations in circuitry began to appear. One of these is the Venturi-type circuit, which combines characteristics of the back-pressure gages discussed above and the flow-type gage to be described below.

Venturi-Type Circuit

In this gage, compressed air at regulated pressure enters a large venturi chamber and then passes through the venturi throat into the smaller venturi chamber where velocity is higher and pressure lower than in the larger chamber. From the smaller chamber the air passes out through the metering orifices in the gage tooling.

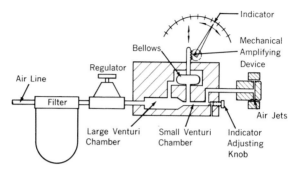

A pressure tube from the large chamber allows the higher pressure of that chamber to act on the outside of an enclosed bellows. A similar tube from the smaller chamber is connected to the inside of the bellows to oppose the pressure in the bellows chamber. The spring action of the bellows in conjunction with this pressure differential causes the bellows to deflect until it reaches equilibrium. This bellows movement, amplified by a rack and pinion, moves a pointer over a graduated dial.

Differential Circuit

The so-called differential circuit is somewhat similar to the Venturi circuit in its use of a bellows, subject to pressure differential, and its rack and pinion amplifier.

Pressure regulated air passes into two separate channels, each having an initial fixed restrictor. One channel, which feeds the bellows cavity, contains an atmospheric bleed for zeroing.

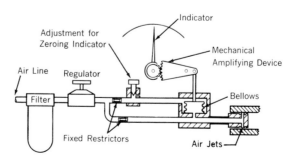

The other channel, connected to the bellows interior, terminates at the orifices of the gage tooling. The pressure differential in the two channels causes the bellows to deflect until equilibrium is reached. This movement registers the back-pressure in the system during the gaging operation on a circular dial scale.

Bourdon Tube Circuit

The Bourdon tube gage is another example of the back-pressure gage. Filtered air from the plant supply passes through a pressure regulator and a metering restrictor into the gaging circuit. Included in the circuit is a connection to a Bourdon tube which deflects with circuit pressure changes. These deflections are again amplified by a rack and pinion mechanism and registered on a circular dial.

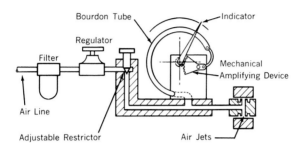

The back-pressure gage has consistently performed well in the progress of industrial metrology where it is often preferable to all other types. However, gage engineers, mindful of the trend toward progressively smaller manufacturing tolerances, wanted to devise some means of raising air gage amplifications without slowing response.

After considerable research, the flow-type principle was announced in 1940. It combined high magnification with swift response in the familiar Sheffield Precisionaire® Column Instrument.

Flow-Type Circuit

By metering the velocity of air flowing in the gaging circuit, amplifications up to 100,000:1 and even higher may readily be attained.

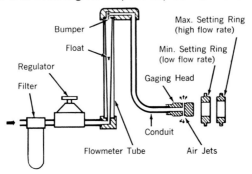

The flow type circuit is the simplest of all air gaging circuits. It is unique in that it is completely pneumatic, involving only the flow of air and the movement of a float. It is not complicated by auxiliary mechanical elements.

Filtered air at regulated pressure passes up through a vertical transparent tube having a tapered bore, the smallest diameter at the bottom. An indicator float in this tube is free to move in response to air flow. When no air is flowing, the float remains at the bottom of the tube. As air in the circuit begins to flow, the float starts to rise. The greater the air velocity, the higher the float will rise.

The air leaving the top of the float tube is passed through the escape orifices or jets in the gage tooling. During the gaging operation, the greater the clearance between these jets and the surface being gaged, the greater the velocity in the pneumatic circuit. Therefore the position of the float in the transparent tube indicates the amount of clearance between tooling and work part surface. Float position is read on a graduated scale alongside the tube, the graduations being in decimals.

The outbreak of World War II brought an unprecedented demand for ordnance of all kinds — a demand which the Allies were ill-prepared to meet, especially in the very critical field of ordnance inspection. Gaging equipment at the time was pitifully inadequate, as was the supply of skilled inspectors.

Gages previously used to inspect small and medium caliber arms required far too much time and skill to meet this emergency. Had it not been for the new air gaging equipment and technique, which so greatly increased the tempo of inspection and de-emphasized inspection skill, it is questionable how the crisis could have been resolved.

Early Developments

The outstanding developments of the 50's, 60's and 70's have been largely in the field of tooling and masters as well as the integration of air gaging with other manufacturing operations, such as, machine controls, automatic gaging and automatic assembly.

Standard tooling for the inspection of bearings, paper, cotton, and other man made fibers were introduced in the 50's and continue to be used in these industries today.

The development of the "Plunjet" gaging cartridge in the 50's by the Sheffield Corporation, allowed part tolerances of up to 0.080 to be measured using air gages. These gaging cartridges greatly simplified the design of multiple circuit gage tooling.

The selection of mating parts, so necessary for the manufacture of precision pumps and servo valves for the automotive and missile industries, is being accomplished by high amplification air gages commonly referred to as "Selectionaire's." Thus, the technique of "match" fitting of parts forms one of the cornerstones of modern mass production manufacturing methods and its use has become wide spread throughout this country.

During the early years, pneumatic gaging was confined to inspecting internal diameters. Since then tooling has been developed which makes it practical to inspect all characteristics of an inside or outside diameter, including size, taper, ovality and straightness. All other external dimensions, such as lengths, flatness, concavity, convexity, center distance, parallelism, squareness, and concentricity can easily be measured using air gages.

The absence of mechanical contact allows for the inspection of easily deformed parts or those with highly polished surfaces. Air gaging also provides the ability to inspect very small bores with a self cleaning action and low maintenance. Low operator skill requirements and the design flexibility offered to the gage designer have made air gaging one of the most universally used gaging systems in the world today.

electrical gages

The practical application of mechanical-electric methods to dimensional gaging made its appearance during the second decade of this century both in this country and in Europe.

It became apparent to those studying the subject that electrical characteristics might well be utilized as a means of gage amplification. Also, it appeared that the high sensitivity of the electrical limit-switch could be very useful when coupled with mechanical gage amplification.

Credit should be accorded to such men as R. Widdington and J. J. Dowling for their pioneering work with oscillatory circuits, and to R. S. Johnson for his work at the Bureau of Standards on strain gaging.

The "Electrolimit" Gage

Doctor Ford of the Admirality Research Laboratory in 1922 suggested electromagnetic induction as a practical means of gage amplification. This is the principle around which General Electric and Pratt & Whitney later developed the now familiar "Electrolimit" gage, during the late twenties and early thirties.

As developed, the Electrolimit Gage was an indicating comparator, utilizing a balanced bridge coil circuit so arranged that any mechanical displacement of the gaging spindle unbalanced the magnetic field of the two opposing electromagnetic coils. The amount of imbalance thus caused was recorded by a sensitive ammeter graduated to read in increments of an inch. Amplification of this gage was easily adjusted by changing the amount of air gap between the coils. Amplifications up to 10,000:1 were readily attained.

With these early gages, fluctuations in line voltage interfered with gage reliability — a difficulty since remedied by more effective voltage regulation.

The "Electrigage"

The "Electrigage," introduced in 1929 by the Sheffield Machine and Tool Company (later The Sheffield Corporation), was the first commercial limit comparator to incorporate electric signal lights to indicate whether the part being gaged was within tolerance, oversize, or undersize. This gage did not indicate the arithmetical value of a dimension.

One of the first of these gages was sold in 1929 to Reo Motors where it served satisfactorily for many years. It is now part of a display of early gages in the Smithsonian Institution in Washington.

Basically, the "Electrigage" head is an extremely sensitive limit switch. Amplification is entirely mechanical, accomplished by the frictionless reed mechanism described above, and later used in the "Visual Gage." The needle arm of this reed mechanism swings in response to gaging spindle displacement. The swing causes the arm to make and break adjustable electrical contacts and thus indicate the size of the part being gaged. Maximum and minimum tolerance limits for the adjustable contacts are set by masters or gage blocks.

Since the function of the electrical current here is merely that of signaling, voltage fluctuations had no effect on gage reliability.

The "Multicheck Electrigage"

The "Multicheck Electrigage" brought out by the Sheffield Gage Corporation in 1934 was the next step in the evolution of the limit-switch principle used in the "Electrigage."

"Electrigage" heads were small and compact. By mounting a number of them on a suitable chassis with a precise work-positioning fixture, multiple dimensions could be gaged simultaneously. Each gaging spindle actuated its own signal, so that each dimension could be inspected individually.

In addition, a single master light integrated all the signals. When the master light showed clear, the work part was passed as acceptable with no need for reference to the individual dimension signals. This proved to be a big time saver in the urgent inspection of mass-produced parts. Without the Multicheck, it would have been almost impossible to gage adequately the millions of ordnance parts needed during World War II.

General Campbell, Commandant of the Frankford Arsenal at that time, cites the service of one of these gages used to inspect five critical dimensions of 37 mm. shells. From the time it was installed in 1940 until the middle of 1944, this gage inspected 5,815,665 shells — 29,078,325 individual dimensions. This one gage saved more than 4000 days of inspection time over previous ordnance gaging precedures. During World War II, gages of the Multicheck type inspected over a billion of the dimensions of ordnance parts.

Automatic Gages

The evolution of the Electrigage principle did not stop even with the "Multicheck." "Electrigage" heads, which could actuate relays just as well as signal lights, became the sensing units of the early automatic gages and also the early automatic machine controls.

Other Types of Circuits

The acceptance of these first electric gages was a sufficient challenge to gagemakers at large to accelerate their activity in this field. Other types of circuits were soon to follow.

Electrical circuits for indicating comparators differed chiefly in the electrical characteristics by which the pickup head or transducer was designed to operate. These involved output voltage, output inductance, output resistance and output capacitance. Many such electrical circuits are in current use.

In order to get increasingly higher amplifications, electronics came into use in connection with conventional electric circuits. In this way gage head outputs were amplified many times before being rectified or detected by the meter circuit. Both electrical and electronic circuits are used in automatic gaging installations today.

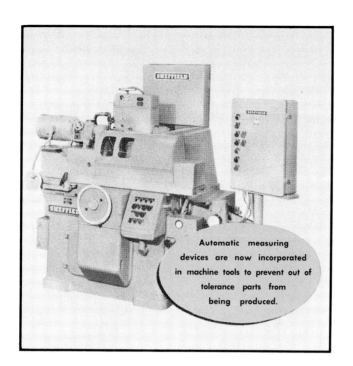

Automatic measuring
devices are now incorporated
in machine tools to prevent out of
tolerance parts from
being produced.

gaging progress in the mid twentieth century

Comparators available to industry by 1940 included the dial indicator, the electric gage, the reed mechanism gage, the air gage and the multiple gage — all considerably more sensitive and more dependable for close tolerance work than the old fixed-size gages which preceded them. Not withstanding these obvious advantages, many manufacturers, including prominent organizations in the automotive and domestic appliance industries, continued to cling to fixed-size gaging, a procedure which was not only tedious but which required many experienced inspectors.

   With few exceptions gaging was still a post-process manual operation. There were a few automatic gages at the beginning of the forties, but only a few. Western Electric had used them for more than a decade.

The Ford Motor Company had automatic gages for checking crankshafts, camshafts, push rods, and valve tappets. Automatic gages were also in use for checking wire, strip metal and bearing balls.

Ball-Race Size Control Gage

An interesting example of automatic machine size control of the early forties was the device used by ball bearing manufacturers for the grinding of ball races. This consisted of a Sheffield "Electrichek" gage head, the gaging contact of which rode the surface of the race being ground throughout its machining cycle. Governed by the size information thus transmitted to the reed mechanism of the gage head, relays were actuated to control coolant flow and spindle movement. The sensitivity of this gage was well within .00005".

An Improved Automatic Ball Checker

By 1943 a new automatic bearing ball checking machine went into service to help break a serious bottleneck in the war production of ball bearings. This unit simultaneously checked and sorted bearing balls at a rate of from 15,000 to 20,000 per hour, doing in one hour what had previously been considered a full day's quota. Balls from 1/8" to 11/16" were segregated by size into 10 precise classifications differing by as little as .00005".

Gaging at the Machine

In the early forties, it was practice to allow processed parts to reach final inspection before being checked for size. By then, if any maladjustment of the processing machine or cutting tool had occurred, a large batch of rejects would have accumulated.

Thus, in order to save time and reduce scrap, gagemakers instituted a crusade for the purpose of supplying each production machine operator with a gaging instrument, right at his machine. This permitted him to check each part as it was finished and thus catch any mechanical trouble before a lot of scrap parts had been produced. This effort was reasonably successful.

External Dimensions Gaged by Air

In 1944 the scope of the air gage was materially broadened. While this gage had long since established its proficiency in the field of internal gaging, it then became equally applicable to precision external gaging. This was the result of the introduction by the Sheffield Corporation of a new air snap gage.

Non-Contact X-Ray Gage

The non-contact X-ray gage made its appearance in 1946 and soon found ready acceptance in the rolling mills.

The X-ray gage operates on the principle that a given material will absorb X-rays passing through it in direct proportion to its thickness. Thus, by metering the X-ray absorption through a given sample and comparing it with that of a known standard, the thickness of the material being gaged was determined.

This gage provided rolling mill management with a continuous thickness check of sheet or strip as the material came from the rolls. It has since become the sensing element of automatic mill roll adjustment mechanisms.

Automatic Cylinder Bore Gage

By 1946 Buick Motor Division of General Motors put into operation the first automatic cylinder bore gaging machine of the type which was to set the general pattern for the industry. It was developed around the flow-type principle of air gaging, such as is used in the "Precisionaire®" air gage.

This machine simultaneously checked eight cylinder bores at four points in each bore for actual diameters and for any out-of-round condition to an accuracy of .0001". It classified each cylinder in increments of .0003" for the selective assembly of pistons. All this was done in less than 60 seconds — a spectacular saving in inspection time and in inspection floor space required.

Operation was almost completely automatic. Cylinder blocks were delivered to the gage, positioned, and removed automatically. The only requirement of the operator was that he swing the lever-controlled gaging spindles through 180 degrees to check out-of-round condition, and to stamp the classification code number on each cylinder bore as indicated by its respective gage reading.

Statistical Quality Control

Statistical quality control emerged as a new science in the field of mass-production. While its scope goes beyond dimensional control, the latter is one of its important phases and one that stresses the need for precision instrument gages of the indicating type.

A productive quality control program was instituted in the Gillette Safety Razor organization in 1946. The Ford Motor Company in 1949 introduced statistical quality control in all its principal divisions. Since then it has spread progressively through the manufacturing community.

Computers and Numerical Machine Control

Considering the trend of development at the time, it was not strange that there should be a rebirth of interest in the possibilities of computers and numerical machine control, the all but forgotten ideas of an earlier period.

The pioneers in this field had been Jacquard, Lanson, Babbage, and others who were reasonably successful even without the benefit of twentieth century electrics, electronics, and pneumatics.

Vannevar Bush, working at the Massachusetts Institute of Technology in 1930, had succeeded in constructing a machine to solve differential equations mechanically.

With the aid of electronics, high-speed digital computers were developed in 1945 by International Business Machines at the Harvard Computation Laboratory.

Considerable work on the numerical control concept was done by the Parsons Corporation of Traverse City, Michigan, under a contract with the Air Materiel Command. Further work, also sponsored by the Air Force, which included an experimental numerically controlled milling machine, was undertaken in 1949 at the Servomechanisms Laboratory of M.I.T.

The Arma Corporation in 1949, with Doctor Fredrick Cunningham cooperating, introduced a numerically controlled tool maker's lathe. This machine proved to be an interesting exhibit of the possibilities of this technique, but it was not successful commercially.

Before the close of the decade, a large number of automatic gaging machines had been put into service. These were used for checking shock-absorber pistons, automotive pistons, and piston rings.

The "Micronaire" Gage

Toward the end of the forties, a new gage known as the "Micronaire®" instrument was developed by Sheffield to facilitate the accurate determination of the fineness of textile fibers — a characteristic very important to that industry, but one which previously had required tedious laboratory work for its determination.

The "Micronaire" instrument is another type of pneumatic gage. A weighed sample of fiber is placed in the specimen cylinder of the gage and compressed to a constant volume. Compressed air at constant pressure is then blown through the sample, and resistance to this air flow is metered. Resistance is in direct proportion to fiber fineness.

Since its introduction, "Micronaire" measurement has become the official standard of industrial, scientific, and governmental agencies dealing with textiles throughout the world.

As our economy entered the fifties, nearly five years of peace had allowed industry to catch up somewhat on the pent-up demand for consumer goods.

Our armed forces had been reduced to but a shadow of their wartime strength, and much of our expensive material had been allowed to deteriorate seriously because of insufficient maintenance personnel. Defense spending dropped to a little more than ten billion dollars.

Thus, when General Douglas McArthur was ordered to stop the Communist's drive into South Korea, he had neither adquate manpower nor the equipment to do a workmanlike job. Defense spending then started another rapid climb that reached 56 billion by the time Korean hostilities ceased in the summer of 1953.

The decade of the fifties was one of industrial expansion. It was further characterized by a shortage of engineers, rapid growth of monopolistic labor union power, skyrocketing wages and prices. In other words, it was an ideal climate for stimulating more extensive and more inclusive automation.

Emphasis during this decade was largely on the refinement and elaboration of basic automation techniques. Some of the outstanding developments were the introduction of air and electronic gaging pickups, development of self-contained electro-pneumatic control units, and accent on automatic assembly.

Pneumatic and Electronic Pickup Cartridges

The introduction by Sheffield in 1952 of the "Plunjet" air gaging cartridge greatly extended the scope and flexibility of air gaging and its use as a means of automatic machine control.

The "Plunjet" cartridge is a sensing or pickup unit used with any type of air gage. It consists essentially of an air valve having a precisely varying orifice area and a mating, spring-urged conical plunger. The opposite end of the plunger is the gaging contact. The position of the plunger determines the effective orifice area and therefore the rate of flow through the orifice and the back pressure behind it. Any change in either flow or back pressure while gaging is directly proportional to plunger travel. By metering this change, plunger travel is determined and registered on the scale of the gaging instrument.

Prior to this, air gaging was not generally considered applicable to broad tolerance applications because of the 0.005" range limitation. The "Plunjet" increased this at least to 0.100".

Because of its small size the "Plunjet" could readily be incorporated in gaging fixtures of all kinds, especially in multi-dimension fixtures. The first practical jet engine turbine blade gage was based on the "Plunjet" which checked 18 dimensions simultaneously. It greatly simplified gaging fixture design not only for specific dimensions, but for the checking of geometrical relationships of elements in an assembly. The "Plunjet" cartridge has proven equally effective as a control for grinding, turning, boring, and honing machines.

Transformer principles had been in use for some time to obtain dimensional measurements with vacuum tube amplifiers. These efforts were handicapped by the size of the transducer and the size of the electronics. The precursor of Linear Variable Displacement Transducer (LVDT) gaging technology of the '70's and '80's was brought out in 1956 by Sheffield. The "Electrojet" unit was based upon the use of LVDT principles. A magnetic core whose position (or displacement from null) produces out-of-phase signals from two opposed secondaries of a small transformer. Careful design keeps the combined signal errors insignificant and permits fast accurate measurements to be made, even of millionths.

Its size often accommodates direct measurements far more economically than more elaborate mechanical designs to using larger units. The real advantage was to be realized when transistors and then integrated circuit technology permitted multi-dimensional checks to be performed on automatic gages and housed in small, reasonably sized enclosures.

Self-Contained Electro-Pneumatic Control Units

The air gage as a solo instrument had a single function: that of dimensional evaluation with the result shown visibly on a scale. When the air gage became an integral part of the automation symphony, a second function was added. Some action on the basis of dimensional findings had to be taken. That action might be to allow a machine to continue operation or to stop it. It might be to change from roughing to finishing cuts. It might be to transfer a part to a succeeding operation, to classify it, or reject it as scrap. The possibilities were and are unlimited.

Such actions are conveniently accomplished by servomechanisms, usually driven electrically. Pneumatic gage action then has to be translated into electrical energy. The fact that high-speed machine tools are often involved makes it highly desirable to accomplish this translation in a minimum time interval.

Thus it was that the "Airelectric" gage head was developed in the early nineteen fifties. This device was a limit-type pneumatic size-control system capable of making and breaking electric contacts. It is sensitive to pressure variations in the pneumatic gaging circuit as small as .05 psi.

Shortly thereafter, the "differential" gaging head was introduced. This unit operated by comparing the pressure difference in two identically calibrated pneumatic sensing circuits. At a selected differential the gage head functioned to initiate the electrical impulse.

By adding an adapter to the "differential" head the element of memory was introduced to produce the "variation" head. This unit is capable of remembering a specific pneumatic pressure and comparing it to transient pressures encountered later. Gage action occurs when the remembered and transient pressures are equal.

These units are applicable either to individual production machines or to automatic production lines for initial checking, machining, or forming, assembly and inspection.

Automatic Assembly

Automatic assembly was the inevitable sequel to automatic processing. Before 1950, however, very little progress in this phase of automation had been made.

Some sporadic interest in assembly became apparent in 1951 and 1952. The Ford Motor Company installed a machine in the Cleveland Engine Plant for the automatic assembly of pistons and piston rings.

By 1954 the metalworking press was giving this subject extensive editorial attention. That year also marked the introduction of three new publications dedicated to automation: "Automation," "Automatic Control," and "Control Engineering." By the middle of the decade, automatic assembly had become accepted as an integral part of automation.

One problem encountered in automating assembly was that of the selective matching of mating elements. Although such parts were processed within their respective tolerance limits, it was not always feasible to assemble them indiscriminately. For instance, a high limit piston could not always be assembled with a low limit cylinder. Automatic precision gaging thus became the basis for selective matching as it was for size control in automatic sequence machining.

"Autometrology"

The idea was very aptly expressed by W. Fay Aller of Sheffield in 1956 when he coined the term "autometrology" to connote the integration of measurement with machining, handling, and memory, to achieve complete automation.

By the end of 1956, a variety of assemblies were being made automatically. Typical among them were automotive cylinder blocks, hydromatic turbine or torus units, telephone and radio equipment, ammeter frames, radiator caps, vacuum valves, automobile tie-rod sockets, roller skate wheels, and distributor caps. Organizations engaged in projects of this type included various divisions of the automotive industry, National Automatic Tool Company, the Cross Company, Western Electric, Bell Telephone Laboratories, Omer E. Robbins Company, Ferguson Machine and Tool Company, and Snyder Tool & Machine Co.

In 1957 the Sheffield Corporation developed a machine for automatically assembling and performing final inspection of roller bearings at the rate of 1000 per hour. After the gaging of diameter and flange thickness of the inner race, the proper number of rolls are selected from one of six storage hoppers. Races, rollers, and cage are then assembled and the bearing checked for torque, standout, and noise. Shortly thereafter, an assembly machine somewhat similar to this was developed for ball bearing assembly.

Further Progress in Machine Control

Subsequent to the work on numerical machine control at M.I.T. previously discussed, many more installations were made on profilers, skin mills, spar mills, jig borers, and internal grinders.

Other recent types of control are the photoelectric line follower and the magnetic tape control. In the former, a photoelectric scanning head follows a line drawing of the part being machined and this controls the machine's operation. In the latter, a recording on magnetic tape is made of the sequence of operations a proficient machinist makes in performing the machining job in question. When this tape is fed back to the machine, the machine automatically repeats each operation in the same sequence as it was recorded.

Machine tool builders aware of the trend began design revisions to better accommodate automation. Some even began the development of their own automatic control equipment.

By 1954 "closed loop" process control had been well established by combinations of mechanical, pneumatic, electrical, and electronic size-sensing units feeding back through various types of servo-mechanisms.

The "Monitorecord®" Instrument

As automated systems became more sophisticated and more elaborate, a higher order of skill became necessary for their set-up and adjustment. The coordination of system circuits for optimum performance often requires split-second timing — in many cases beyond the capability of the human eye and stop watch.

To cope with this situation, the "Monitorecord" instrument was introduced in 1957 by Sheffield. This device is a portable precision timing instrument. When plugged into the nervous system of an automated installation, it efficiently produces a strip chart of the concurrent actions of the several circuits. By comparing this chart with a transparent master, discrepancies are immediately spotted and evaluated on a precise time scale.

The Eli Whitney Metrology Laboratory

Indicative of the progressive importance of greater dimensional precision to American industry in this period, was the dedication of the Eli Whitney Metrology Laboratory by Louis Polk, February 17, 1956.

This was America's first industrial Standards Laboratory, designed, constructed, and equipped in accordance with practices accepted by the great national standards laboratories of the United States, Great Britain, France, and Germany. It is qualified in both staff and facilities to supplement the work of these national laboratories in calibrating and certifying dimensional standards for industry — services previously available in this country only at the Bureau of Standards in Washington.

Besides standards calibration, this laboratory makes dimensional audits of precision components, develops overall dimensional control programs for industry at large, and carries on a continuing program of metrology research.

automation

It might be asked how a chapter on automation belongs in a history of measurement. In fact, the two are so closely interrelated that neither can or should be considered separately. Measurement is not only essential to modern automation, but to all industrial production. As it has aptly been said: "You can't make what you can't measure because, otherwise, you wouldn't know whether or not you had made it."

The fact of automation was recognized, and the idea accepted, long before the term came into use. The term itself was coined by Delmar S. Harder, a Ford Motor Company production executive in 1948. It happened when plans for a model change were being made. New production machines were to be installed and a new production line laid out. Competitive pressure was a strong motivating force as it usually is in automotive planning; so production costs were a critical factor.

When Harder said "What we need is more AUTOMATION," he referred to a better mechanical means of stepping up the rate of flow of parts in process along the production line — ways to reduce the time consumed by loading, unloading, and transfer of parts from machine to machine. At the time, this represented a sizable portion of overall cost.

The meaning of the term, as Harder used it, has been progressively expanded by an accelerating technology, to include such other automatic functions as machining, size control, inspection, sorting, counting, weighing, assembly, testing and packaging — in other words, complete production systems.

Genesis of Automation

Early accomplishments in automation date back to the 18th century. Notable among them were:

1780 — Oliver Evans' automatic grist mill.
1801 — Brunel's mechanized pulley block shaping machine.
1804 — J. M. Jacquard's loom controlled by punched cards.
1860 — Automatic screw machine of Brown & Sharpe.
1887 — Tolbert Lanson's Monotype (typesetting machine) controlled by punched tape.

1913 — Ford's mechanized assembly line.
1920 — A. O. Smith's automatic automobile frame plant.
1921 — John Shaw invented the Keller duplicating system.
1924 — Transfer machine in the Morris automobile plant, in Coventry England.
1929 — Graham-Page cylinder block transfer machine.
1948 — Fully automatic connecting rod gage designed and manu-factured by Sheffield for Ford Motor Company.
1950 — Numerical control systems developed to operate machine tools.
1958 — Kearney and Trecker's Machining Center with 4 axis NC control, tool changer and pallet shuttle.
1961 — Industrial Robot used in automotive assembly plant.

Notwithstanding the attractive potential indicated by these early efforts, automation in the modern sense did not start to attract attention until about 1940. There were several reasons.

For the previous ten years, this country had had to bear a devastating economic depression. Employment and wage rates were both very low — not a propitious situation in which to launch new labor-saving ideas and thus to compound further the distress of unemployment.

There were other reasons as well. Supporting technology was progressing slowly, except perhaps in the field of measurement. We lacked adequate experience with electronics and with servomechanisms. The first thorough treatment of the servomechanism theory by Hazen was scarcely six years old.

World War II

International tensions were the most potent factor in revitalizing our economic climate and industrial activity.

Hitler invaded Poland, September 1, 1939. Britain and France imme-diately accepted the challenge and World War II was launched. The United States began to plan for what seemed inevitable.

The prohibition of munitions sales to Europe decreed by the Neutrality Act of 1937 was recinded. By 1940 the United States Army and Navy had embarked on an expansion program which included the acqui-sition of ultra-modern weapons and munitions.

Thus was industry alerted to the probable need for a new high order of precision in manufacture and vastly increased manufacturing production.

Then came the holocaust at Pearl Harbor with its inescapable challenge to all industry. Machine production shot up from $3,000,000 in June of 1940 to $1,300,000,000 by September of 1942. The sales curve for industrial recording and controlling instruments showed a similar precipitous climb from its 1940 base.

Industry shouldered this tremendous responsibility, but under the serious handicap of "Selective Service." The draft was no respecter of persons. "Greetings" came to the skilled inspector and the seasoned machinist as well as to the farmer and retail clerk.

Industry was forced to devise ways to compensate for the loss of experienced craftsmen to the armed forces, without lowering the quality or quantity of its production. The pinch was especially critical in the ranks of trained inspectors.

The obvious answer was in the use of inspection instruments which, by their design, de-emphasized the need for human skill and experience — instruments that by-passed human frailty. In other words, there seemed to be no alternative to automation.

Modern Day Automation

Automation in the inspection area gained tremendous progress through the 60's, accelerated rapidly in the 70's and is now part of almost every machining or assembly system as we go through the 80's.

Automatic gaging comes in many forms, but in all cases the decision as to the parts quality is removed from the operator, and made by the machine.

In Process Gaging — Direct Control

One popular type of automatic gaging is In-Process Direct Control on grinders which has the gage mounted on the same machine where the operation is performed. This gaging system continuously measures the part during the machining process and provides feedback control signals to the machine.

When the workpiece is very close to its final dimension, the in-feed of the grinding wheel is automatically stopped, and allows the part to dwell. When the exact on-size is reached, the grinding wheel is automatically retracted.

In-Process Gaging — Indirect Control

This type of system is sometimes called post-process gaging. In this system the part is measured immediately after it is ejected from the machine to detect drift and to generate, as a trend, the appropriate machine control signals. Examples of this type of machine control are seen on thru-feed centerless grinders, or double disc grinders.

In-Process — Station Type Gaging (Integrated Gaging)

This type of gaging system is also referred to as on-line, in-line or post process gaging. This gaging system is not generally mounted on the machine where the operation was performed, but is located before the next operation, and before final inspection. In this system automatic signals are fed back to the machine to actuate various controls.

Most common control is automatic machine stoppage to indicate a reject condition or tool failure.

Automatic tool compensation is fast becoming very popular. Compensation is based on the status of the workpiece generated either by a specified number of warning signals or by statistical information.

Semi-Automatic Gage

This type of gage is generally used for low production, where the loading and unloading time is not critical to the thru-put. The operator manually positions the part into the load station or directly into the gage station and initiates the start cycle. All gaging, including rotation as necessary, is done automatically. Conditions being gaged could be as few as a single diameter to as many as fifty dimensions measured simultaneously as on a crankshaft.

Automatic Gage

Automatic gages are used in most production systems. Part handling and controls are integrated into the synchronized gaging system.

Fully automatic gaging plays a dramatic role in the success of the automated factory. It must be carefully planned in advance and fully integrated into the total scheme of manufacture, part-handling, chip removal, cleaning, part-disposal and communication control.

Automatic gaging performs several tasks. Most important, it removes rejected parts out of the system, but it also, in many cases, provides signals to automatically compensate tools, make adjustments, initiate alert signals for self-diagnosis and provides a wealth of information for counting and other statistics used to evaluate system operation and effectiveness.

The key to successful automated factories is to control the process so closely that rejects are almost non-existent due to immediate, automatic correction of equipment problems.

surface texture measurement

Surface metrology may be broadly defined as the measurement of the difference between what the surface actually is and what it is intended to be. It is treated separately from length measurement because length measurement is concerned with the relationship of two surfaces on a workpiece, whereas surface measurement is involved with the relationship of a surface on the workpiece to a reference which is not actually on the workpiece. The most common aspect of surface metrology is the measurement of surface roughness as an averge deviation from a mean center line.

Stylus System of Measurement

The most common way to measure surface finish is to move a stylus over the surface and measure an average electrical signal produced by a transducer attached to the stylus. Other means used less frequently include stylus profiling where a chart record is produced instead of an average number, reflectance meters, pneumatics, and optical interference. The stylus averaging unit is most common because it is fast, repeatable, quite easy to interpret, and relatively inexpensive.

Stylus systems embrace the following essential elements: the surface, the stylus, the drive to move the stylus with respect to the surface, the reference, the amplifier, and the data presentation.

The first stylus type surface finish instrument was developed by E. J. Abbott, founder of Physicists Research, in the early 1930's.

Surface Measurement Systems

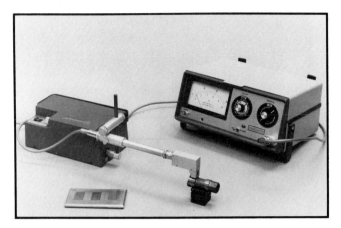

Profilometer

Today there are two prevalent stylus-type surface measuring systems: averaging and profiling.

Averaging systems trace a surface and indicate a numerical value for the roughness average. (See above illustration.)

Profiling systems are more versatile and may be used to display charts of the total profile, the waviness profile, and the roughness profile as well as the average roughness. In recent times these instruments have been interfaced to computers for control, data analysis and data presentation.

measurement of roundness

Geometrically, a part can be said to be round, in a given cross section, if there exists within the section a point from which all points on the periphery are equidistant. In practice, however, the radius of nominally round parts tends to vary from point to point. Thus the problem found by the metrology engineer is one of displaying and assessing these variations, and correctly interpreting the results.

In general, roundness specifications are intended to control part-feature form as opposed to part-feature size or roughness. Until recently the specification and measurement of roundness and other geometrical relationships have not been adequately covered by national or company standards. In fact, specification of roundness on blueprints in most cases is usually insufficiently defined to ensure proper measurement and interpretation of the part form. Only recently has it been recognized by industry that the more commonly employed roundness-measurement techniques have severe limitations, even though the first practical roundness instruments were developed in the early 1950's.

What is "Out-of-Roundness"?

All surfaces of circular cross section are originally generated by revolving about, or with reference to, fixed points, axes, or lines of contact in a machine tool such as centers, work spindles, steady rests, tool edges, and grinding-wheel surfaces. However, the relationship of these points, axes, and lines of contact, and the parts, is never truly fixed. Variable deflections and imperfect rotation occur as the surface is generated because of imbalance, erratic cutting action, inadequate lubrication, non-uniform temperatures, wear, defective or improper machine parts, and geometry. The result is usually a deviation from roundness in the form of waves about the circumference of the part. These are generally identified as so many waves, lobes, or undulations about the circumference. The number of lobes can vary from two to several hundred about the circumference of the cross section. Two, three, five, seven, and nine lobed parts are common results of manufacturing processes. Out of roundness may also result from distortion of the part by chuck jaws, fixturing, localized heating, excessive feeds, and warped or out-of-round stock.

Measurement Methods

While many methods have been used for roundness measurement, only those which provide valid radial-deviation data lend themselves to standardization and consistent and accurate measurement of all out-of-roundness conditions. For this reason current industry, national, and international standards cover primarily measurements taken with precision-spindle-type instruments with the data recorded on a polar chart.

Much of the out-of-roundness measurement performed in industry is by techniques, such as the use of V-blocks, which have limitations that are not generally recognized. These techniques, while they are not accurate or dependable, may be of some value if their limitations are recognized and their use does not prejudice the function of the part.

Precision Spindle Methods

The two major types of precision-spindle instruments are those in which the spindle supports and rotates the part with the gage tip remaining stationary, and those in which the spindle rotates the gage tip about the part, which remains stationary.

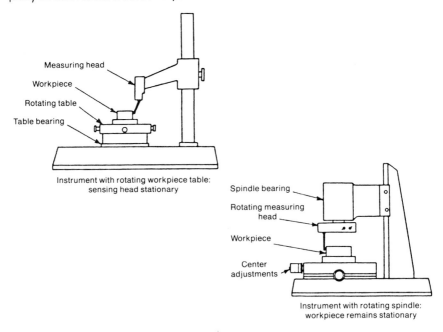

Measuring head
Workpiece
Rotating table
Table bearing

Instrument with rotating workpiece table: sensing head stationary

Spindle bearing
Rotating measuring head
Workpiece
Center adjustments

Instrument with rotating spindle: workpiece remains stationary

System of roundness measurement with extrinsic datum.[1]

106

The center of rotation of the precision spindle and the indicator gage tip provides a master radius to which all the radii of a cross-section profile of the part are compared. It is necessary that the center of the part cross section and the spindle axis be adjusted to be concentric within the narrow limits. The variations of the cross-section radii from the master radius are usually recorded in a highly magnified form on a polar chart.

The magnified profile produced on the polar chart is evaluated by two concentric circles which just contain the profile when centered in accordance with the minimum-radial-separation center criteria. Other center criteria can be specified. The two concentric circles can be drawn with a bow compass or more commonly are visually selected from a number of concentric circles engraved on a transparent overlay. The out-of-roundness value is the separation of the two concentric circles containing the charted profile divided by the magnification setting of the instrument.

The polar chart clearly shows the number and magnitude of the roundness deviations. There are many advantages to the precision-spindle methods.

Accurate measurements of all types of out of roundness are possible and a permanent polar-chart record which is easily interpreted is provided. It is also the most accurate method of measurement available. With proper equipment, accuracies of 1 millionth of an inch are attainable. In addition to roundness, the equipment also permits ultra-precise measurement of concentricity, squareness, flatness and other related geometric part-feature characteristics.

The limitations are a comparatively high initial investment, and the method cannot be used economically on very large parts.

Bench Center Method

Bench centers and a precision mechanical, air, or electronic indicator may be used to measure part out of roundness on a radial basis and can produce results equivalent to the precision-spindle method. There are many limitations to this method.

Parts must have center holes or be adaptable to mounting on a mandrel with center holes. The measurement accuracy is affected by shape and angle of centers and center holes, location and alignment of centers and center holes, lubrication of center, straightness of part surface. These factors must be controlled to a much greater degree than the roundness accuracy desired.

V-Block Method

Addition of a V-block anvil to any diameter of gaging device is one of the most commonly employed techniques for measuring out of roundness. This addition converts the diameter measurement to a chordial-height variation, and presents a new set of measurement peculiarities which are dependent upon the included angle of the V-anvil and the number of lobes present on the part circumference. Some lobing conditions are greatly magnified and others are reduced or not detected at all. Irregularly spaced lobing is also difficult to detect or assess.

Apollo Series Cordax® Coordinate Measuring Machine

coordinate measuring machines

The industrial expansion of the 50's brought increased complexity and productivity demands with requirements for quality improvements. The introduction of numerical control of machine tools in this same time period caused production attention to often shift from the manufacturing area to the inspection area.

The inspection of dimensional size and location of various features such as holes, surfaces and centerlines on a "first part" manufactured by an NC machine tool was a slow and tedious process. Two or three dimensional coordinate measurement was limited to the use of open set-up surface plate equipment. Skilled inspectors labored long over complex parts to determine if dimensions were in accordance with the tolerances given on drawings. The process was difficult, involved, and totally dependent on the elimination of human errors.

All measurements were comparative, made with single-axis gage blocks, height stands, dial indicators and other special equipment. Part alignment and multiple orientations required much care and complicated fixturing. The judgement of the inspector was critical to the interpretation of the results. All data was manually recorded and all angles, tolerances and sizes were individually calculated. Productivity improvements in the machining process had moved the production bottleneck downstream to the measurement process and open set-up surface plate inspection techniques just could not keep pace.

In the summer of 1959, a new concept of coordinate measurement was introduced at the International Machine Tool Show in Paris by Ferranti Limited, a Scottish firm. This first coordinate measuring machine with an accuracy of .001 inch was initially a two-axis device designed for locating holes in the face of a part. It consisted of a pair of free moving perpendicular horizontal axes, each having a read-out of position and carrying a short travel vertical axis. A removeable tapered probe was inserted in the vertical axis and placed into the holes. Vertical pressure centered the probe and the position of the hole was read on the X and Y displays.

The need for greater measuring ranges, a third axis, improved accuracies and peripheral equipment soon became apparent. In 1965, the Cordax® family of coordinate measuring machines was introduced by Sheffield. This second generation family of machines provided expanded measuring range with accuracies about twice the original Ferranti machines and incorporated many new features such as .0001" resolution, elevating tables, and a printout attachment.

Coordinate measuring machines (CMM's) developed since the initial entries into the market continue to maintain the same basic elements of design. Distinct physical configurations of CMM's in use today include the cantilever, horizontal arm, traveling bridge, fixed bridge, jig bore and overhead bridge or gantry design machines. Each design was developed to meet specific application needs with individual advantages and disadvantages. All designs incorporate the same basic fundamental concept of three coordinate axes, each square in its own relationship to the reference plane created by the other two axes.

Each axis is fitted with a reference system and a linear measurement transducer for positional feedback. This allows position displays within the measuring envelope to be independent of any fixed reference point. The most common reference systems in use are stainless steel scales and glass scales. Both systems utilize non-contact electro-optical counters for determining exact position of the reading head. Stainless steel reference scales are widely used in shop environments. The similarity between the stainless steel material used for the scales and the part will cause both to react to the temperature environment in the same manner. Glass scales are capable of superior accuracy but are susceptible to differential temperature changes in non-controlled environments due to the difference in coefficient of expansion between the glass scale and the metal part.

Computer-Assisted CMM's

The value of Coordinate measuring machines was soon recognized by the manufacturing community. Seeking to extend the versatility and usefulness of the CMM small general-purpose digital mini-computers were offered to simplify error and tolerance calculations and two dimensional part-to-machine axis alignment. This new capability significantly reduced the time required for set-up, recording and off-line data analysis.

Direct Computer-Control

Although the mini-computer brought the full utilization of the CMM's potential closer to realization, the problem of operator errors and productivity in the inspection of parts with numerous dimensional features remained. Human operators of machines are subject to distraction and boredom and tend to be inconsistent in the performance of repetitive tasks of even short duration. These factors led to the development of the first fully automatic CMM.

In 1969, a computer-controlled CMM was shown by Sheffield at the ASTME Show. This machine was capable of checking two-dimensional location of holes in a flat plate using a tapered probe. The machine positioned the tapered probe into the hole and released it allowing the probe to center itself in the hole for recording.

Electronic Probes

The utility of a measuring machine depends largely on the nature of the probing device.

Use of taper probe tips was the most universal application but the user had to be aware when relying on the hole edge and taper surface, that an error of approximately .0001" could be present in most instances. This error could be considerably larger with changes in surface and hole characteristic. It was this inherent error, when using the taper probe principle, that prompted the development of the tramming probe/electronic amplifier assembly. This assembly used the tramming probe adapter, Sheffield Electronic Feathertouch Gage Head. With this unit the coordinate measuring machine user could tram the hold or surface, use the amplifier meter scale as a fiducial and thus establish the true X-Y coordinate position completely ignoring hole or surface characteristics.

Even though this was a major improvement in the ability to utilize a CMM for dimensional inspection, it still did not meet most needs.

In 1975, the 3-D electronic touch probe was introduced by Renishaw Ltd, England. Since that time, the 3-D electronic touch probe has become widely used on coordinate measurement machines. This probe is an omni-directional triggering device consisting of a probe body and stylus. When attached to the moving 3rd axis of a CMM, a sensitive electrical contact in the probe detects any deflection of the stylus caused by contact with a workpiece. Upon deflection, a signal is provided indicating the scale positional data for each axis. Using this signal and the computer allowed us fast coordinate data acquisition. Calculation of offset angles of the part to the machine's axes allowed mathematical three-axis part alignment to be done quickly and easily, eliminating the need to spend the time to manually align a part.

The Measurement Processor

It was soon evident that a system was needed that could easily be understood by quality engineers, manufacturing engineers and inspectors, none of whom had any significant experience with computers. Machine shop personnel would not be able to program parts for inspection unless the programming procedure was simplified.

In 1978, a significant step forward was made in CMM data processing capability with the introduction of the Measurement Processor (MP) by Sheffield. It marked the first time that a low-cost microprocessor was incorporated into a CMM system.

The concept of the measurement processor is to place a microprocessor's data processing circuitry between the position transducers on the measuring machine and the position displays. The result is a low-cost digital readout with built-in, powerful, but easy-to-use data collection and analysis functions for manual CMM's. The MP provides basic data processing capability previously available only with a general purpose computer or calculator system while allowing workpart coordinates to be displayed instead of machine coordinates.

The heart of the MP is a measurement-function library, a collection of commonly used measurement routines that can be called up by entering a simple number code through a set of pushbuttons. These functions are resident in the microprocessor's permanent memory and are therefore instantly available. No additional software needs to be loaded into the system. The simplicity of the system made it easy for even the least-skilled operator to use.

The initial Measurement Processor was designed to offer basic measurement data processing capability for manual CMM's while minimizing the ease of operation, but many inspection problems require sophisticated three-dimensional geometry solutions that the initial MP did not address.

In 1981, Sheffield introduced a new Measurement Processor series of data processing equipment to meet the needs of medium and highly complex measurement problems. Microprocessor support was also provided to control all positional moves on the totally automated DCC machines.

Distributed data processing control systems combined with multi-axes probe heads, sophisticated 3-D software and simple operator-friendly (self-teach) systems are working to dramatically enhance the through-put of CMM's.

Higher Performance Machines

In 1986 Sheffield introduced their new Apollo Series of Cordax Machines that embodied a new philosophy of design and a unique configuration.

The traveling axis forms a complete ring which provides for an extremely stiff structure. The bearing way surfaces for the traveling ring structure are on a frame that is completely independent of the table with this arrangement. The weight of heavy parts to be measured does not affect machine accuracy.

With the very stiff ring construction the Apollo Cordax is able to provide exceptional repeatability. Geometry errors are corrected by complex algorithms involving 21 error parameters. The National Bureau of Standards provided valuable consultation on error correction methodology.

The Apollo Cordax has its drive axis on the center line of the ring which provides for excellent dynamic performance when operated in the automatic mode.

Future Developments

Increasing emphasis is being placed upon the total integration of the manufacturing process into a systematic, cohesive and automated system. The automated factory of the future embodies this concept and will attempt to automate and integrate all the aspects of manufacturing including, planning, design, machining, inspection, assembly and test. The closed-loop process will ultimately increase productivity and product quality while lowering cost. The complete solution of this concept has not yet taken form but the step-by-step, so-called "Automated Factory" is approaching.

A key element of this evolving Automated Factory is flexible manufacturing systems, (FMS) adaptable to various products, models or materials. Essential to the long-term success of FMS is in-line gaging and inspection with real-time feedback to keep the manufacturing processes within specification. The coordinate measuring machine is the natural means to perform the dimensional inspection tasks in the Automated Factory. An automatic CMM, being a highly flexible measuring device, can measure parts of virtually any configuration or complexity without special gages or fixturing.

Recent advances in coordinate measuring machine system technology is making possible and practical the linkage of flexible inspection systems to flexible, automatic manufacturing.

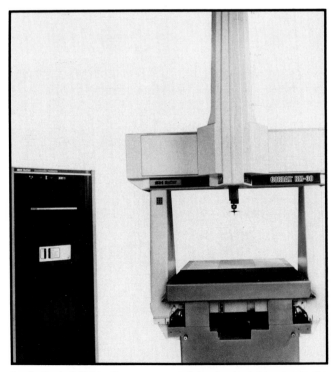

Apollo Cordax® CMM with covers removed showing ring bridge construction

production optical gaging

In the 1980's, the advent of reliable laser sources, high speed micro-processors, precision linear photodiode arrays and solid state TV cameras has provided the building blocks to produce practical production optical gaging systems.

Many systems are now being used for accurate dimensional measurement and surface flaw detection.

Basic Principle

The basic principle of Production Optical Gaging is that light is emitted from a controlled source and presented to the object to be inspected. This light is either reflected as a measure of the object's distance or is modified in some way by the object's presence. This modification is then sensed and related to the variable being measured.

Types of Dimensional Gaging Systems

There are four major types of systems which have provided practical solutions to production gaging problems:

Scanning Laser

One system consists of a low powered laser which is formed into a thin beam of light. This beam, through a rotating mirror, scans the measurement area at a constant speed. The object being measured interrupts this beam for a period of time which is proportional to the diameter or thickness of the part being measured. This system can produce results with a resolution of 10 millionths of an inch. It is particularly useful for measuring the diameter of moving wire.

Linear Array

Another system consists of a light source which emits parallel light beams from one side of an object to be measured. A photo optical diode array is located on the opposite side. The diameter of the object is measured by the number of elements of the array which are blocked off. This system has no moving parts and can resolve dimensions to a 50 millionth of an inch or less depending on the range of the photo diode array. Large diameters can be measured by utilizing two diode arrays, one on each side of the part. This is a very high speed system limited only by the rate that the individual photo diode elements or pixels can be electronically scanned and the data processed by a microcomputer.

Triangulation

The triangulation type optical sensors are used to accurately measure the distance from the probe to a part surface. When the part position and the probe position are known, the signal from this sensor indicates the part dimension. A representative type system uses a controlled light source to create an illuminated spot on the surface to be measured. A portion of this light is scattered and picked up by a detector in the same manner that an image would be focused on the back of the human eye. A variation in the position of the measured surface results in a change of location of the reflected light at the sensor, thus identifying the position of the surface. One application of this type of sensor is as a probe on a coordinate measuring machine where a combination of the probe signal and the axis position of the gage gives an accurate part dimension.

TV Camera

A system which comes the closest to reproducing the eyes of an inspector is a TV camera which digitizes the picture that it sees. The digitized picture is compared to a stored picture and can determine part orientation and feature presence. This requires a large amount of data processing and hence is slower than scanning lasers, linear arrays and triangulation systems. Much development is being done in this area. Dimensions can also be measured but again not with the resolution of the previously described systems.

Surface Gaging

Surface gaging refers to determining surface conditions with light reflections. This requires signature analysis of reflected light which can give an indication of surface finish or presence of surface flaws. Highly refined software is required to provide useful output signals.

Conclusion

Optical gaging is in the early stages on application. With the rapid advancements being made in electro-optical and computer science technologies the use of optical sensing for gaging will greatly increase.

controls of the 80's

Feedback

Feedback can be defined as supplying information as to how closely the actual output of a process matches the desired output. In the machining process feedback information concerns itself with comparing gaged part dimensional data with blueprint tolerances for that part.

Measurement, the heart of all feedback, is what metrology is all about. It is necessary to measure the difference between a gaged part's dimensional data versus blueprint tolerances. The purpose of this book, so far, has been to provide the reader with the history of measurement in metrology and gaging transducers in general. Now, it is of interest to consider what can be done with that gaging information.

The human body is the most complicated feedback mechanism ever designed. It comes equipped with five methods of monitoring process outputs, namely the five senses. These monitoring methods are unreliable at best because there is no way of calibrating them. Therefore, all measurements taken with them are subjective. As dimensional requirements become tighter, the human senses are not equipped to accurately provide the feedback information necessary for machining processes. As man developed his measurement standards, he also developed ways of letting machines take these measurements for him.

Man was able, through the use of instruments such as vernier calipers, to measure the dimensional part information he needed. This enabled him to interpret that data and adjust his machining processes accordingly. In a parallel effort, with developing his measurement standards, man also strived for automation. Through this science, he let machines take over many of the more mundane tasks associated with measurements by feeding back the information to the machine process directly. Employing mechanical and electrical feedback systems in this manner is referred to as automation. Automatic machines were used to increase the net production of a process as compared to what humans could do in a more manual approach. Using machines with feedback frees the operator to perform other tasks, thereby increasing his productivity.

The history of using feedback methods to control system processes dates back to Greece around 250 B.C. There, a clock was designed using a float regulator to control the timing necessary to build a clock. It was also during that period that float regulators were designed for oil lamps to maintain a constant level of fuel. Heron of Alexandria published a book titled, PNEUMATICA, during the first century A.D. This book described several mechanisms that utilized float regulators to control water levels.

Progress in developing feedback control systems was relatively slow. It wasn't until around 1600 that temperature regulators were designed. The first pressure regulator, which was used on a steam boiler, was invented in 1681. This regulator was designed for safety and is very similar to the regulator found on pressure cookers today.

The governor, designed by James Watt in 1769 for controlling the speed of a steam engine, is generally considered to be the first automatic feedback controller used in industrial processes. This all-mechanical device used centrifugal force from a power takeoff of a steam engine to control the amount of steam from the boiler into the engine. It is interesting to note that this development in feedback control technology coincided with the advances in metrology and machining processes. Once it became possible to machine and build the engine it became necessary to design the control devices to operate the system.

Up until 1868, it was necessary to design feedback control systems by intuitive feeling. Then pioneers, such as J. C. Maxwell, were able to provide mathematical descriptions of processes and the mechanics to control them. The advent of the vacuum tube generated more progress. Bode, Nyquist and Black of the Bell Telephone Laboratories introduced electronic feedback amplifiers. World War II itself added great impetus in the design and development of control systems. Through those efforts, designs for automatic pilots for airplanes, gun positioning systems and radar antenna control systems were developed. In 1957, the first commercially available transistors provided the basis necessary for our present day, relatively low cost, electronic control systems. These systems utilize such tools as the high speed, digital computer.

Many present day metrology machines are equipped with automatic feedback. These machines usually have air to electronic or strictly electronic gaging transducers. Electrical signals from transducers represent the acutal measured parameters of a machined part from a given machining process and are then sent to a computer or a process controller for interpretation.

Process controllers compare the dimensional information of the machined part with the desired dimensional tolerances for the part. These machines even have the capability of removing any parts which do not meet dimensional specifications and placing them in a reject category.

Statistics

Today, as the cost of computer memory keeps coming down, it becomes economical to increase the power of these process controllers even further. The increased computing power of process controllers is being utilized in today's factories to provide statistical analysis of a processes' machining capabilities. Statistics is a science of making generalizations, predictions or estimating the relationships between two or more variables.

Taking measurements from a small sample group of an overall population of parts produced from a machine permits certain predictions to be made. These predictions have a relatively high amount of certainty whether or not all the parts are within part specification.

Statistical inference can also be made on such parameters as tool life. Taking measurements as to how many parts can be machined from a given tool until the tool needs to be changed because it is worn out, allows the statistician to predict an average life for tools used under those same conditions.

This type of data then made it possible to build more completely automatic machining processes. Many machines have automatic tool compensation and are used to maintain a continued production of good quality parts.

Diagnostics

The computer power of machines today make it possible to program them for self diagnostics. Assume that a machining process is continually producing parts that are within the tolerance specification. The feedback control system relays the measurement information to the process controller for statistical analysis. Assume that the next part measured by the feedback system is way outside the specification tolerance limits. The statistical analysis, inside the process controller, determines that a catastrophic error has crept into the system, such as breakage of the machining tool. The controls of the machining tool have the intelligence programmed into them to shut down the machining process until the repairs can be effected because no further parts are likely to be produced that are within machine tolerance. A warning signal, such as a flashing lamp, can be used to alert the human operator that repairs are required.

The diagnostic programs being incorporated in today's process controllers, are becoming so powerful that they can monitor every aspect of material handling in the machining process. In the case of completely automated factories, these powerful diagnostic programs inform maintenance personnel as to the nature of a failure of equipment within the system. These diagnostic programs check for jammed parts, empty part feeders, full reject chutes. The process controllers even check themselves to see if they have broken down.